The Canterville Ghost

THE GRAPHIC NOVEL
Oscar Wilde

ORIGINAL TEXT VERSION

Script Adaptation: Seán Michael Wilson
Linework: Steve Bryant
Additional Inking: Classical Comics Ltd
Colouring: Jason Millet
Lettering: Jim Campbell
Design & Layout: Jo Wheeler,
Carl Andrews & Jenny Placentino

Editor in Chief: Clive Bryant

The Canterville Ghost: The Graphic Novel
Original Text Version

Oscar Wilde

First UK Edition

Published by: Classical Comics Ltd

Acknowledgments: Every effort has been made to trace copyright holders of
material reproduced in this book. Any rights not acknowledged here will be
acknowledged in subsequent editions if notice is given to Classical Comics Ltd.

All enquiries should be addressed to:
Classical Comics Ltd.
PO Box 7280
Litchborough
Towcester
NN12 9AR
United Kingdom
Tel: 0845 812 3000

info@classicalcomics.com
www.classicalcomics.com

ISBN: 978-1-906332-27-3

A catalogue record for this book is available from the British Library.

Printed in the UK

This book is printed by ESP Colour Limited using biodegradable vegetable inks,
on environmentally friendly paper which is FSC (Forest Stewardship Council)
certified (SA-COC-001904). This material can be disposed of by recycling,
incineration for energy recovery, composting and biodegradation.

Contents

Dramatis Personæ

The Ghost
Sir Simon de Canterville

Lord Canterville
An English Lord

Mr. Hiram B. Otis
An American Minister

Mrs. Lucretia R. Otis
Wife of Mr. Hiram B. Otis

Washington Otis
Son of Mr. & Mrs. Otis

Virginia Otis
Daughter of Mr. & Mrs. Otis

The "Stars and Stripes"
Twin Sons of Mr. & Mrs. Otis

Cecil
The Duke of Cheshire

Mrs. Umney
The Housekeeper at Canterville Chase

Prologue

The year is 1886.

Deep in the heart of the English countryside stands
Canterville Chase — a large country mansion that has
been in the Canterville family for hundreds of years.
It is an impressive house in an idyllic setting and, while
it is little wonder that the members of the American Otis
family are so keen to live there, a few questions remain:

Why is such a grand house for sale in the first place?

What can possibly be wrong with it?

Why doesn't Lord Canterville want to live there himself?

There can only be one explanation...

   ...one that anyone who has ever been to
   Canterville Chase knows only too well...

   ...the house is haunted by

The Canterville Ghost

WHEN *MR. HIRAM B. OTIS*, THE AMERICAN MINISTER, BOUGHT *CANTERVILLE CHASE*, EVERY ONE TOLD HIM HE WAS DOING A VERY *FOOLISH* THING, AS THERE WAS *NO DOUBT* AT ALL THAT THE PLACE WAS *HAUNTED*.

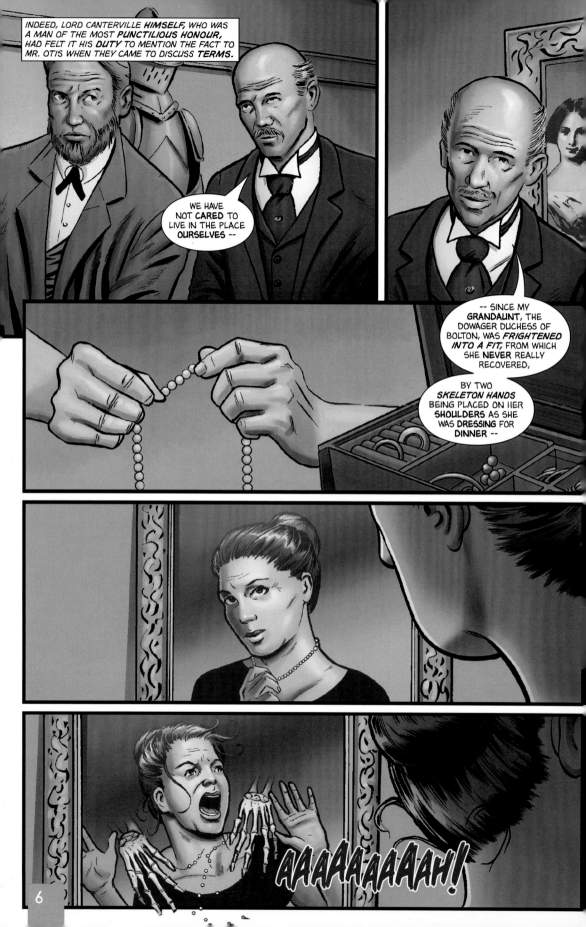

I HAVE COME FROM A **MODERN** COUNTRY, WHERE WE HAVE **EVERYTHING** THAT **MONEY** CAN **BUY;**

AND WITH ALL **OUR** SPRY YOUNG FELLOWS PAINTING THE OLD WORLD **RED,** AND CARRYING **OFF** YOUR BEST **ACTORS** AND **PRIMA-DONNAS,** --

-- I RECKON THAT IF THERE **WERE** SUCH A THING AS A **GHOST** IN EUROPE, WE'D HAVE IT AT HOME IN A **VERY** SHORT TIME IN ONE OF OUR PUBLIC **MUSEUMS,** OR ON THE ROAD AS A **SHOW.**

I **FEAR** THAT THE **GHOST** EXISTS,

THOUGH IT MAY HAVE **RESISTED** THE **OVERTURES** OF YOUR ENTERPRISING **IMPRESARIOS.**

IT HAS BEEN WELL KNOWN FOR **THREE** CENTURIES,

SINCE 1584 IN FACT, --

-- AND *ALWAYS* MAKES ITS APPEARANCE BEFORE THE *DEATH* OF ANY MEMBER OF OUR FAMILY.

WELL, SO DOES THE **FAMILY DOCTOR** FOR THAT MATTER, LORD CANTERVILLE.

BUT THERE IS **NO SUCH** THING, SIR, AS A *GHOST,* --

-- AND I GUESS THE **LAWS OF NATURE** ARE NOT GOING TO BE **SUSPENDED** FOR THE BRITISH **ARISTOCRACY.**

YOU ARE CERTAINLY VERY *NATURAL* IN AMERICA, --

-- AND IF YOU DON'T *MIND* A **GHOST** IN THE HOUSE, IT IS ALL RIGHT.

ONLY YOU **MUST** REMEMBER *I WARNED YOU.*

A FEW WEEKS AFTER THIS, THE PURCHASE WAS **CONCLUDED,** AND AT THE CLOSE OF THE SEASON THE MINISTER AND HIS FAMILY WENT DOWN TO **CANTERVILLE CHASE.**

MRS. OTIS, WHO, AS MISS **LUCRETIA R. TAPPAN,** OF WEST 53rd STREET, HAD BEEN A **CELEBRATED** NEW YORK **BELLE,** WAS NOW A VERY **HANDSOME,** MIDDLE-AGED WOMAN, WITH FINE **EYES,** AND A SUPERB **PROFILE.**

MANY **AMERICAN** LADIES ON **LEAVING** THEIR NATIVE LAND ADOPT AN APPEARANCE OF CHRONIC **ILL-HEALTH,** UNDER THE IMPRESSION THAT IT IS A FORM OF EUROPEAN REFINEMENT, BUT MRS. OTIS HAD **NEVER** FALLEN INTO THIS **ERROR.** SHE HAD A **MAGNIFICENT** CONSTITUTION, AND A REALLY **WONDERFUL** AMOUNT OF **ANIMAL SPIRITS.**

INDEED, IN MANY RESPECTS, SHE WAS QUITE **ENGLISH,** AND WAS AN **EXCELLENT** EXAMPLE OF THE FACT THAT WE HAVE REALLY **EVERYTHING** IN **COMMON** WITH AMERICA NOWADAYS...

... EXCEPT, OF COURSE, **LANGUAGE.**

HER ELDEST SON, CHRISTENED *WASHINGTON* BY HIS PARENTS IN A MOMENT OF *PATRIOTISM*, WHICH HE NEVER CEASED TO *REGRET*, WAS A RATHER GOOD-LOOKING YOUNG MAN, WHO HAD *QUALIFIED* HIMSELF FOR AMERICAN *DIPLOMACY* BY *LEADING* THE GERMAN AT THE NEWPORT *CASINO* FOR *THREE* SUCCESSIVE *SEASONS*, AND EVEN IN *LONDON* WAS WELL KNOWN AS AN EXCELLENT *DANCER*.

GARDENIAS AND THE *PEERAGE* WERE HIS *ONLY* WEAKNESSES. OTHERWISE HE WAS *EXTREMELY* SENSIBLE.

MISS VIRGINIA E. OTIS WAS A LITTLE GIRL OF FIFTEEN, LITHE AND *LOVELY* AS A *FAWN*, AND WITH A FINE *FREEDOM* IN HER LARGE BLUE *EYES*.

SHE WAS A *WONDERFUL AMAZON*, AND HAD ONCE *RACED* OLD LORD BILTON ON HER *PONY* TWICE ROUND THE PARK, *WINNING* BY A LENGTH AND A HALF, JUST IN FRONT OF THE *ACHILLES STATUE*...

...TO THE HUGE *DELIGHT* OF THE YOUNG *DUKE OF CHESHIRE*, WHO *PROPOSED* FOR HER ON THE SPOT, AND WAS SENT BACK TO *ETON* THAT VERY NIGHT BY HIS GUARDIANS, IN FLOODS OF *TEARS*.

AFTER VIRGINIA CAME THE *TWINS*, WHO WERE USUALLY CALLED *"THE STARS AND STRIPES"*, AS THEY WERE ALWAYS GETTING *SWISHED*.

THEY WERE *DELIGHTFUL* BOYS, AND, WITH THE EXCEPTION OF THE WORTHY *MINISTER*, THE ONLY TRUE *REPUBLICANS* OF THE FAMILY.

THEY **STARTED** ON THEIR DRIVE IN **HIGH SPIRITS.** IT WAS A **LOVELY** JULY EVENING, AND THE AIR WAS **DELICATE** WITH THE **SCENT** OF THE **PINE-WOODS.**

NOW AND THEN THEY HEARD A **WOOD-PIGEON** BROODING OVER ITS OWN SWEET **VOICE,** OR SAW, DEEP IN THE RUSTLING FERN, THE BURNISHED BREAST OF THE **PHEASANT.**

LITTLE **SQUIRRELS** PEERED AT THEM FROM THE BEECH-TREES AS THEY WENT BY, AND THE **RABBITS** SCUDDED AWAY THROUGH THE BRUSHWOOD AND OVER THE MOSSY KNOLLS, WITH THEIR WHITE **TAILS** IN THE AIR.

AS THEY ENTERED THE *AVENUE* OF CANTERVILLE CHASE, HOWEVER, THE *SKY* BECAME SUDDENLY *OVERCAST.*

AWRKK
AWRRKK
AWWRK

STANDING ON THE STEPS TO RECEIVE THEM WAS AN *OLD WOMAN.*

THIS WAS *MRS. UMNEY,* THE *HOUSEKEEPER,* WHOM MRS. OTIS, AT LADY CANTERVILLE'S EARNEST REQUEST, HAD CONSENTED TO *KEEP* IN HER *FORMER POSITION.*

I BID YOU WELCOME TO CANTERVILLE CHASE.

FOLLOWING HER, THEY PASSED THROUGH THE FINE TUDOR HALL...

...INTO THE LIBRARY.

I AM AFRAID SOMETHING HAS BEEN SPILT THERE.

YES, MADAM, *BLOOD* HAS BEEN SPILT ON THAT SPOT.

HOW HORRID! I DON'T AT ALL CARE FOR *BLOOD-STAINS* IN A SITTING-ROOM.

IT MUST BE REMOVED AT ONCE.

IT IS THE BLOOD OF LADY ELEANORE DE CANTERVILLE,

WHO WAS *MURDERED* ON THAT VERY SPOT BY HER OWN HUSBAND, SIR SIMON DE CANTERVILLE, IN 1575.

SIR SIMON *SURVIVED* HER *NINE* YEARS, AND DISAPPEARED SUDDENLY UNDER *VERY MYSTERIOUS CIRCUMSTANCES.*

HIS BODY HAS *NEVER* BEEN DISCOVERED, BUT HIS GUILTY SPIRIT STILL *HAUNTS* THE CHASE.

MY DEAR HIRAM, **WHAT** CAN WE **DO** WITH A WOMAN WHO **FAINTS?**

CHARGE IT TO HER LIKE **BREAKAGES;** SHE WON'T **FAINT** AFTER **THAT.**

*IN A FEW **MOMENTS** MRS. UMNEY CERTAINLY **CAME TO.***

I HAVE **SEEN** THINGS --

-- WITH MY **OWN** EYES, SIR, THAT WOULD MAKE ANY CHRISTIAN'S *HAIR STAND ON END* --

-- AND **MANY** AND **MANY** A NIGHT I HAVE **NOT CLOSED MY EYES** IN **SLEEP** FOR THE *AWFUL THINGS* THAT ARE **DONE** HERE.

*MR. OTIS, HOWEVER, AND HIS WIFE WARMLY **ASSURED** THE HONEST SOUL THAT THEY WERE **NOT** AFRAID OF **GHOSTS,***

*AND, AFTER INVOKING THE BLESSINGS OF **PROVIDENCE** ON HER NEW MASTER AND MISTRESS, AND MAKING ARRANGEMENTS FOR AN INCREASE OF **SALARY,** THE OLD HOUSEKEEPER TOTTERED OFF TO HER OWN ROOM.*

CHAPTER II

THE **STORM** RAGED **FIERCELY** ALL THAT NIGHT...

...BUT **NOTHING** OF **PARTICULAR** NOTE OCCURRED.

CROAK

THE NEXT MORNING, HOWEVER, WHEN THEY CAME DOWN TO **BREAKFAST**...

...THEY FOUND THE TERRIBLE **STAIN** OF **BLOOD** ONCE AGAIN ON THE FLOOR.

I DON'T THINK IT CAN BE THE **FAULT** OF THE **PARAGON DETERGENT**, FOR I HAVE TRIED IT WITH **EVERYTHING**.

IT **MUST** BE THE **GHOST**.

HE ACCORDINGLY **RUBBED OUT** THE STAIN A **SECOND TIME**.

THE SECOND MORNING...

...IT APPEARED AGAIN.

THE THIRD MORNING ALSO IT WAS THERE, THOUGH THE LIBRARY HAD BEEN LOCKED UP AT NIGHT BY MR. OTIS HIMSELF, AND THE KEY CARRIED UP-STAIRS.

THE WHOLE FAMILY WERE NOW QUITE INTERESTED; MR. OTIS BEGAN TO SUSPECT THAT HE HAD BEEN TOO DOGMATIC IN HIS DENIAL OF THE EXISTENCE OF GHOSTS...

...MRS. OTIS EXPRESSED HER INTENTION OF JOINING THE PSYCHICAL SOCIETY...

...AND WASHINGTON PREPARED A LONG LETTER TO MESSRS. MYERS AND PODMORE ON THE SUBJECT OF THE PERMANENCE OF SANGUINEOUS STAINS WHEN CONNECTED WITH CRIME.

22

THAT NIGHT ALL **DOUBTS** ABOUT THE OBJECTIVE EXISTENCE OF **PHANTASMATA** WERE REMOVED **FOR EVER**. THE DAY HAD BEEN **WARM** AND **SUNNY**; AND, IN THE **COOL** OF THE **EVENING**, THE WHOLE **FAMILY** WENT OUT TO DRIVE.

THE CONVERSATION IN **NO** WAY TURNED UPON **GHOSTS**, SO THERE WERE NOT **EVEN** THOSE PRIMARY CONDITIONS OF RECEPTIVE **EXPECTATIONS** WHICH SO **OFTEN** PRECEDE THE PRESENTATION OF PSYCHICAL **PHENOMENA**.

THE SUBJECTS DISCUSSED WERE MERELY SUCH AS FORM THE **ORDINARY** CONVERSATION OF CULTURED AMERICANS OF THE **BETTER** CLASS, SUCH AS THE IMMENSE **SUPERIORITY** OF MISS FANNY DAVENPORT OVER SARAH BERNHARDT AS AN **ACTRESS**...

...THE **DIFFICULTY** OF OBTAINING GREEN CORN, BUCKWHEAT CAKES, AND HOMINY, EVEN IN THE **BEST** ENGLISH HOUSES;

THE **IMPORTANCE** OF BOSTON IN THE DEVELOPMENT OF THE **WORLD-SOUL**;

THE **ADVANTAGES** OF THE BAGGAGE CHECK SYSTEM IN **RAILWAY** TRAVELLING...

...AND THE **SWEETNESS** OF THE **NEW YORK** ACCENT AS COMPARED TO THE **LONDON** DRAWL.

NO MENTION **AT ALL** WAS MADE OF THE **SUPERNATURAL**...

...NOR WAS **SIR SIMON DE CANTERVILLE** ALLUDED TO IN **ANY WAY**.

AT ELEVEN O'CLOCK THE FAMILY *RETIRED*...

...AND BY *HALF-PAST* ALL THE *LIGHTS* WERE *OUT*.

SOME TIME AFTER...

...MR. OTIS WAS AWAKENED BY A *CURIOUS NOISE* IN THE CORRIDOR, OUTSIDE HIS *ROOM*.

clank

clank clank squeak clank

SLAM

27

FOR A MOMENT THE CANTERVILLE GHOST STOOD QUITE MOTIONLESS IN NATURAL INDIGNATION;

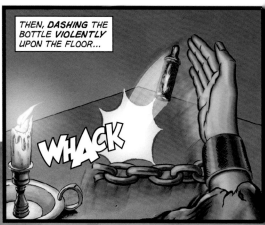

THEN, DASHING THE BOTTLE VIOLENTLY UPON THE FLOOR...

WHACK

...HE FLED DOWN THE CORRIDOR.

OOOHHHHH

clank clank squeak

clank clank

NEVER, IN A BRILLIANT AND UNINTERRUPTED CAREER OF **THREE HUNDRED YEARS,** HAD HE BEEN SO GROSSLY **INSULTED.**

HE THOUGHT OF THE DOWAGER DUCHESS, WHOM HE HAD **FRIGHTENED** INTO A **FIT**...

...OF THE FOUR HOUSEMAIDS, WHO HAD GONE INTO **HYSTERICS**...

...OF THE RECTOR OF THE PARISH, WHOSE **CANDLE** HE HAD BLOWN OUT...

...AND WHO HAD BEEN UNDER THE **CARE** OF **SIR WILLIAM GULL** EVER SINCE...

...AND OF OLD MADAME DE TREMOUILLAC, WHO, AFTER *SEEING* HIM...

...HAD BEEN CONFINED TO HER *BED* FOR *SIX WEEKS* WITH AN ATTACK OF *BRAIN FEVER*...

...AND ON HER *RECOVERY* HAD BECOME RECONCILED TO THE *CHURCH*...

...AND BROKEN *OFF* HER *CONNECTION* WITH THAT NOTORIOUS *SCEPTIC*, MONSIEUR *DE VOLTAIRE*.

HE REMEMBERED THE **TERRIBLE NIGHT** WHEN THE **WICKED** LORD CANTERVILLE WAS FOUND **CHOKING** IN HIS DRESSING-ROOM, WITH THE KNAVE OF DIAMONDS HALF-WAY DOWN HIS THROAT...

...AND **CONFESSED**, JUST BEFORE HE **DIED**, THAT HE HAD **CHEATED** CHARLES JAMES FOX OUT OF **£50,000** AT CROCKFORD'S BY MEANS OF THAT **VERY CARD**...

...AND SWORE THAT THE **GHOST** HAD **MADE** HIM **SWALLOW** IT.

ALL HIS GREAT **ACHIEVEMENTS** CAME **BACK** TO HIM AGAIN...

...FROM THE **BUTLER** WHO HAD **SHOT** HIMSELF IN THE PANTRY BECAUSE HE HAD SEEN A GREEN **HAND TAPPING** AT THE WINDOW-PANE...

...TO THE *BEAUTIFUL LADY STUTFIELD*...

...WHO WAS ALWAYS OBLIGED TO WEAR A BLACK VELVET *BAND* ROUND HER *THROAT*...

...TO HIDE THE *MARK* OF FIVE FINGERS *BURNT* UPON HER *WHITE SKIN*...

...AND WHO *DROWNED* HERSELF AT *LAST* IN THE *CARP-POND* AT THE END OF THE *KING'S WALK*.

WITH THE ENTHUSIASTIC *EGOTISM* OF THE TRUE *ARTIST* HE WENT OVER HIS MOST *CELEBRATED* PERFORMANCES, AND *SMILED BITTERLY* TO HIMSELF AS HE RECALLED TO MIND HIS LAST APPEARANCE AS *"RED REUBEN, OR THE STRANGLED BABE"*...

...HIS *DEBUT* AS *"GAUNT GIBEON, THE BLOOD-SUCKER OF BEXLEY MOOR"*...

33

...AND THE *FURORE* HE HAD *EXCITED* ONE LOVELY *JUNE* EVENING...

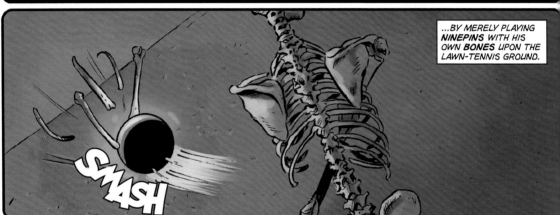

...BY MERELY PLAYING *NINEPINS* WITH HIS OWN *BONES* UPON THE LAWN-TENNIS GROUND.

SMASH

AND AFTER ALL *THIS*, SOME WRETCHED MODERN *AMERICANS* WERE TO COME AND OFFER *HIM* THE RISING SUN *LUBRICATOR*, AND THROW *PILLOWS* AT HIS *HEAD!*

IT WAS QUITE *UNBEARABLE*. BESIDES, NO GHOST IN *HISTORY* HAD EVER BEEN TREATED IN THIS *MANNER*.

ACCORDINGLY, HE DETERMINED TO HAVE *VENGEANCE*, AND REMAINED TILL DAYLIGHT IN AN ATTITUDE OF *DEEP THOUGHT*.

CHAPTER III

THE NEXT **MORNING,** WHEN THE OTIS FAMILY MET AT **BREAKFAST,** THEY **DISCUSSED** THE **GHOST** AT SOME LENGTH.

THE UNITED STATES MINISTER WAS NATURALLY A LITTLE **ANNOYED** TO FIND THAT HIS **PRESENT** HAD NOT BEEN **ACCEPTED.**

I HAVE **NO WISH** TO DO THE GHOST ANY PERSONAL **INJURY,** --

-- AND I MUST SAY THAT, CONSIDERING THE LENGTH OF **TIME** HE HAS BEEN IN THE HOUSE, --

-- I **DON'T** THINK IT IS AT **ALL POLITE** TO THROW **PILLOWS** AT HIM.

HA HA HA HA HA

UPON THE **OTHER** HAND IF HE REALLY **DECLINES** TO USE THE RISING SUN **LUBRICATOR,** WE SHALL HAVE TO TAKE HIS CHAINS **FROM** HIM.

IT WOULD BE QUITE IMPOSSIBLE TO SLEEP, WITH SUCH A NOISE GOING ON OUTSIDE THE BEDROOMS.

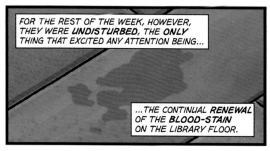

FOR THE REST OF THE WEEK, HOWEVER, THEY WERE *UNDISTURBED*, THE *ONLY* THING THAT EXCITED ANY ATTENTION BEING...

...THE CONTINUAL *RENEWAL* OF THE *BLOOD-STAIN* ON THE LIBRARY FLOOR.

THIS CERTAINLY WAS VERY *STRANGE*, AS THE DOOR WAS ALWAYS *LOCKED* AT NIGHT BY MR. OTIS...

...AND THE WINDOWS KEPT CLOSELY *BARRED*.

THE CHAMELEON-LIKE *COLOUR*, ALSO, OF THE STAIN EXCITED A GOOD DEAL OF COMMENT. *SOME* MORNINGS IT WAS A DULL (ALMOST INDIAN) RED...

...*THEN* IT WOULD BE *VERMILION*...

...THEN A *RICH PURPLE*.

...NCE WHEN THEY CAME DOWN FOR [F]AMILY *PRAYERS,* ACCORDING TO [T]HE SIMPLE RITES OF THE FREE [A]MERICAN REFORMED EPISCOPALIAN [C]HURCH...

...THEY FOUND IT A BRIGHT EMERALD *GREEN.*

THESE *KALEIDOSCOPIC CHANGES* NATURALLY *AMUSED* THE PARTY VERY *MUCH,* AND *BETS* ON THE SUBJECT WERE FREELY MADE EVERY EVENING.

THE *ONLY* PERSON WHO DID *NOT* ENTER INTO THE JOKE WAS LITTLE *VIRGINIA,* WHO, FOR SOME *UNEXPLAINED* REASON, WAS ALWAYS A GOOD DEAL *DISTRESSED* AT THE SIGHT OF THE BLOOD-STAIN...

...AND VERY NEARLY *CRIED* THE MORNING IT WAS EMERALD-GREEN.

37

THE **SECOND** APPEARANCE OF THE GHOST WAS ON **SUNDAY NIGHT.**

SHORTLY AFTER THEY HAD GONE TO BED...

CRASH

...THEY WERE SUDDENLY **ALARMED** BY A FEARFUL **CRASH** IN THE **HALL.**

RUSHING DOWN-STAIRS...

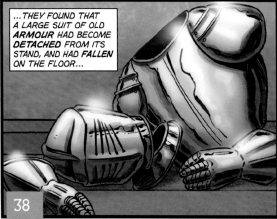

...THEY FOUND THAT A LARGE SUIT OF OLD **ARMOUR** HAD BECOME **DETACHED** FROM ITS STAND, AND HAD **FALLEN** ON THE FLOOR...

...WHILE THE CANTERVILLE **GHOST** WAS RUBBING HIS **KNEES** WITH AN EXPRESSION OF ACUTE **AGONY** ON HIS FACE.

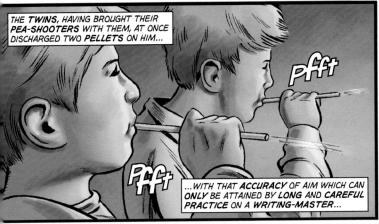
THE *TWINS*, HAVING BROUGHT THEIR *PEA-SHOOTERS* WITH THEM, AT ONCE DISCHARGED TWO *PELLETS* ON HIM...

Pfft

Pfft

...WITH THAT *ACCURACY* OF AIM WHICH CAN *ONLY* BE ATTAINED BY *LONG* AND *CAREFUL* PRACTICE ON A *WRITING-MASTER*...

...WHILE THE UNITED STATES MINISTER *COVERED* HIM WITH HIS *REVOLVER*.

PUT YOUR HANDS UP!

AARRGGGGHHH!

THE GHOST *SWEPT* THROUGH THEM LIKE A MIST...

WOOOOOSH

...EXTINGUISHING WASHINGTON OTIS'S *CANDLE* AS HE PASSED...

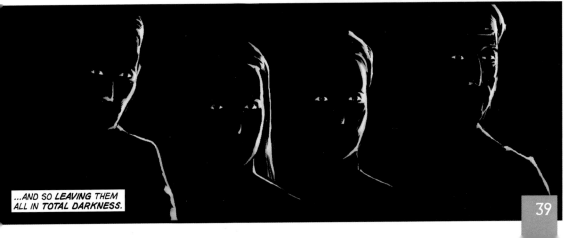
...AND SO *LEAVING* THEM ALL IN *TOTAL DARKNESS*.

ON REACHING THE **TOP** OF THE **STAIRCASE** HE **RECOVERED** HIMSELF, AND DETERMINED TO GIVE HIS CELEBRATED **PEAL** OF **DEMONIAC** LAUGHTER.

THIS HE HAD ON **MORE** THAN ONE OCCASION FOUND EXTREMELY **USEFUL**. IT WAS SAID TO HAVE TURNED LORD RAKER'S WIG **GREY** IN A SINGLE **NIGHT**, AND HAD CERTAINLY MADE **THREE** OF LADY CANTERVILLE'S FRENCH **GOVERNESSES** GIVE WARNING **BEFORE** THEIR **MONTH** WAS UP.

HE ACCORDINGLY **LAUGHED** HIS MOST **HORRIBLE** LAUGH...

HA HA HA MWAHAHA

HA HA MWA HA HA HA

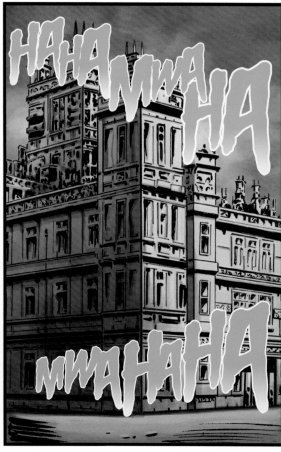

HA HA MWA HA MWAHAHA

BUT HARDLY HAD THE *FEARFUL* ECHO DIED AWAY WHEN A *DOOR* OPENED...

I AM AFRAID YOU ARE *FAR* FROM WELL, --

-- AND HAVE BROUGHT YOU A BOTTLE OF *DR. DOBELL'S* TINCTURE.

IF IT IS *INDIGESTION*, YOU WILL FIND IT A MOST *EXCELLENT* REMEDY.

THE GHOST *GLARED* AT HER IN *FURY*...

...AND *BEGAN* AT ONCE TO MAKE PREPARATIONS FOR TURNING HIMSELF INTO A LARGE BLACK *DOG*...

...AN ACCOMPLISHMENT FOR WHICH HE WAS *JUSTLY* RENOWNED, AND TO WHICH THE FAMILY *DOCTOR* ALWAYS ATTRIBUTED THE PERMANENT *IDIOCY* OF LORD CANTERVILLE'S *UNCLE*, THE HON. THOMAS HORTON.

GROWL SNARL

41

THE SOUND OF APPROACHING *FOOTSTEPS*, HOWEVER, MADE HIM *HESITATE* IN HIS *FELL PURPOSE...*

OOEERRRGH!

Clump de Clump de Clump

≷ SIGH ≷

ON REACHING HIS *ROOM* HE ENTIRELY *BROKE DOWN*, AND BECAME A PREY TO THE MOST VIOLENT *AGITATION.*

THE *VULGARITY* OF THE TWINS AND THE GROSS *MATERIALISM* OF MRS. OTIS WERE NATURALLY EXTREMELY *ANNOYING*, BUT WHAT REALLY DISTRESSED HIM *MOST* WAS THAT HE HAD BEEN *UNABLE* TO *WEAR* THE SUIT OF *MAIL.*

HE HAD *HOPED* THAT EVEN MODERN *AMERICANS* WOULD BE *THRILLED* BY THE SIGHT OF A SPECTRE IN *ARMOUR...*

...AT LEAST OUT OF RESPECT FOR THEIR NATIONAL POET *LONGFELLOW,* OVER WHOSE GRACEFUL AND ATTRACTIVE *POETRY* HE HIMSELF HAD WHILED AWAY *MANY* A WEARY HOUR WHEN THE CANTERVILLES WERE UP IN TOWN.

WHOAH!

YEOUCH!

CRASH

BESIDES, IT WAS HIS *OWN* SUIT.

HE HAD WORN IT WITH *GREAT SUCCESS* AT THE KENILWORTH *TOURNAMENT,* AND HAD BEEN *HIGHLY* COMPLIMENTED ON IT BY NO LESS A PERSON THAN THE *VIRGIN QUEEN* HERSELF.

FOR SOME DAYS AFTER THIS HE WAS *EXTREMELY ILL*, AND HARDLY STIRRED OUT OF HIS ROOM AT ALL, EXCEPT TO KEEP THE *BLOOD-STAIN* IN PROPER *REPAIR*.

HOWEVER, BY TAKING GREAT *CARE* OF HIMSELF, HE *RECOVERED*, AND RESOLVED TO MAKE A *THIRD* ATTEMPT TO *FRIGHTEN* THE UNITED STATES MINISTER AND HIS FAMILY.

HE SELECTED FRIDAY, THE 17th OF AUGUST, FOR HIS APPEARANCE, AND SPENT MOST OF THAT DAY IN LOOKING OVER HIS *WARDROBE*.

TOWARDS *EVENING* A VIOLENT *STORM* OF RAIN CAME ON, AND THE WIND WAS SO *HIGH* THAT ALL THE WINDOWS AND DOORS IN THE OLD HOUSE *SHOOK* AND *RATTLED*.

IN FACT, IT WAS *JUST* SUCH WEATHER AS HE *LOVED*.

44

HIS *PLAN* OF *ACTION* WAS THIS. HE WAS TO MAKE HIS WAY *QUIETLY* TO WASHINGTON OTIS'S ROOM, *GIBBER* AT HIM FROM THE FOOT OF THE BED...

...AND *STAB* HIMSELF THREE TIMES IN THE *THROAT* TO THE SOUND OF *LOW MUSIC.*

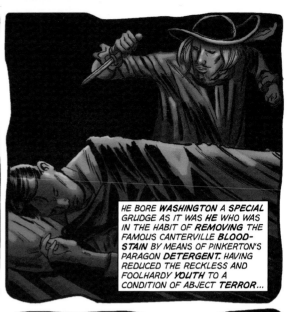

HE BORE *WASHINGTON* A *SPECIAL* GRUDGE AS IT WAS *HE* WHO WAS IN THE HABIT OF *REMOVING* THE FAMOUS CANTERVILLE *BLOOD-STAIN* BY MEANS OF PINKERTON'S PARAGON *DETERGENT.* HAVING REDUCED THE RECKLESS AND FOOLHARDY *YOUTH* TO A CONDITION OF ABJECT *TERROR*...

...HE WAS THEN TO *PROCEED* TO THE ROOM *OCCUPIED* BY THE UNITED STATES *MINISTER* AND HIS *WIFE*...

...AND THERE TO PLACE A CLAMMY *HAND* ON MRS. OTIS'S *FOREHEAD,* WHILE HE HISSED INTO HER TREMBLING *HUSBAND'S* EAR THE *AWFUL* SECRETS OF THE *CHARNEL-HOUSE.*

WITH REGARD TO LITTLE *VIRGINIA,* HE HAD NOT QUITE MADE UP HIS MIND. SHE HAD NEVER *INSULTED* HIM IN ANY WAY, AND WAS *PRETTY* AND *GENTLE.*

OOOO...

A FEW HOLLOW *GROANS,* HE THOUGHT, WOULD BE *MORE* THAN SUFFICIENT, OR, IF THAT *FAILED* TO *WAKE* HER, HE MIGHT *GRABBLE* AT THE COUNTERPANE WITH PALSY-TWITCHING *FINGERS.*

AS FOR THE *TWINS,* HE WAS QUITE *DETERMINED* TO TEACH THEM A *LESSON.* THE *FIRST* THING TO BE DONE WAS, OF COURSE, TO *SIT* UPON THEIR *CHESTS,* SO AS TO PRODUCE THE *STIFLING* SENSATION OF NIGHTMARE. THEN, AS THEIR BEDS WERE QUITE *CLOSE* TO EACH OTHER, TO STAND *BETWEEN* THEM...

HA!

...TILL THEY BECAME *PARALYSED* WITH *FEAR*...

...AND FINALLY, TO *CRAWL* ROUND THE ROOM IN THE CHARACTER OF *"DUMB DANIEL, OR THE SUICIDE'S SKELETON"*...

...A RÔLE IN WHICH HE HAD ON *MORE* THAN ONE *OCCASION* PRODUCED A *GREAT* EFFECT, AND WHICH HE CONSIDERED QUITE *EQUAL* TO HIS *FAMOUS* PART OF *"MARTIN THE MANIAC, OR THE MASKED MYSTERY".*

AT HALF-PAST TEN HE HEARD THE FAMILY GOING TO BED.

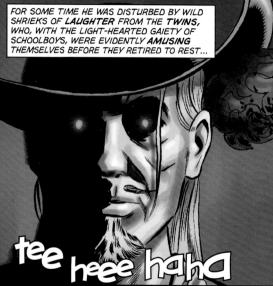

FOR SOME TIME HE WAS DISTURBED BY WILD SHRIEKS OF *LAUGHTER* FROM THE *TWINS*, WHO, WITH THE LIGHT-HEARTED GAIETY OF SCHOOLBOYS, WERE EVIDENTLY *AMUSING* THEMSELVES BEFORE THEY RETIRED TO REST...

tee heee haha

...BUT AT A QUARTER-PAST ELEVEN ALL WAS *STILL*, AND, AS *MIDNIGHT* SOUNDED, HE SALLIED *FORTH*.

THE OTIS FAMILY *SLEPT*, UNCONSCIOUS OF THEIR *DOOM*...

WHOO WHOO

AWWRK

HIGH ABOVE THE RAIN AND STORM HE COULD HEAR THE STEADY **SNORING** OF THE **MINISTER** FOR THE UNITED STATES.

ZZZZZZZZZ

HE STEPPED **STEALTHILY** OUT OF THE WAINSCOTING, WITH AN **EVIL SMILE** ON HIS **CRUEL**, WRINKLED **MOUTH**.

ON AND ON HE **GLIDED**, LIKE AN **EVIL SHADOW**...

ONCE HE THOUGHT HE **HEARD** SOMETHING **CALL**, AND **STOPPED**;

BUT IT WAS ONLY THE **BAYING** OF A **DOG** FROM THE RED FARM, AND HE WENT ON, **MUTTERING** STRANGE SIXTEENTH-CENTURY **CURSES**, AND EVER AND ANON BRANDISHING THE RUSTY **DAGGER** IN THE MIDNIGHT AIR.

FINALLY HE REACHED THE **CORNER** OF THE **PASSAGE** THAT LED TO LUCKLESS **WASHINGTON'S** ROOM. FOR A **MOMENT** HE **PAUSED** THERE...

THEN THE CLOCK **STRUCK** THE QUARTER, AND HE FELT THE **TIME** WAS **COME**.

BONG

HEH HEH HEH...

HE **TURNED** THE CORNER; BUT NO SOONER HAD HE **DONE** SO...

47

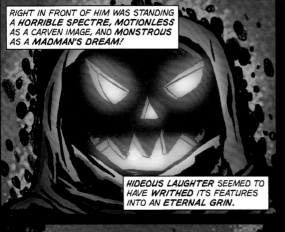

RIGHT IN FRONT OF HIM WAS STANDING A *HORRIBLE SPECTRE*, *MOTIONLESS* AS A *CARVEN IMAGE*, AND *MONSTROUS* AS A *MADMAN'S DREAM!*

HIDEOUS LAUGHTER SEEMED TO HAVE *WRITHED* ITS FEATURES INTO AN *ETERNAL GRIN.*

ON ITS BREAST WAS A *PLACARD* WITH *STRANGE* WRITING IN ANTIQUE CHARACTERS, SOME *SCROLL OF SHAME* IT SEEMED, SOME RECORD OF *WILD SINS*, SOME *AWFUL* CALENDAR OF *CRIME...*

...AND, WITH ITS RIGHT HAND, IT BORE ALOFT A *FALCHION* OF GLEAMING STEEL.

NEVER HAVING SEEN A *GHOST* BEFORE, HE NATURALLY WAS TERRIBLY *FRIGHTENED...*

...AND HE *FLED* BACK TO HIS ROOM, *TRIPPING UP* IN HIS LONG WINDING-SHEET AS HE *SPED* DOWN THE CORRIDOR...

...AND FINALLY *DROPPING* THE RUSTY DAGGER INTO THE MINISTER'S JACK-BOOTS, WHERE IT WAS *FOUND* IN THE *MORNING* BY THE *BUTLER.*

slam

ONCE IN THE **PRIVACY** OF HIS **OWN APARTMENT**, HE **FLUNG** HIMSELF DOWN ON A SMALL PALLET-BED.

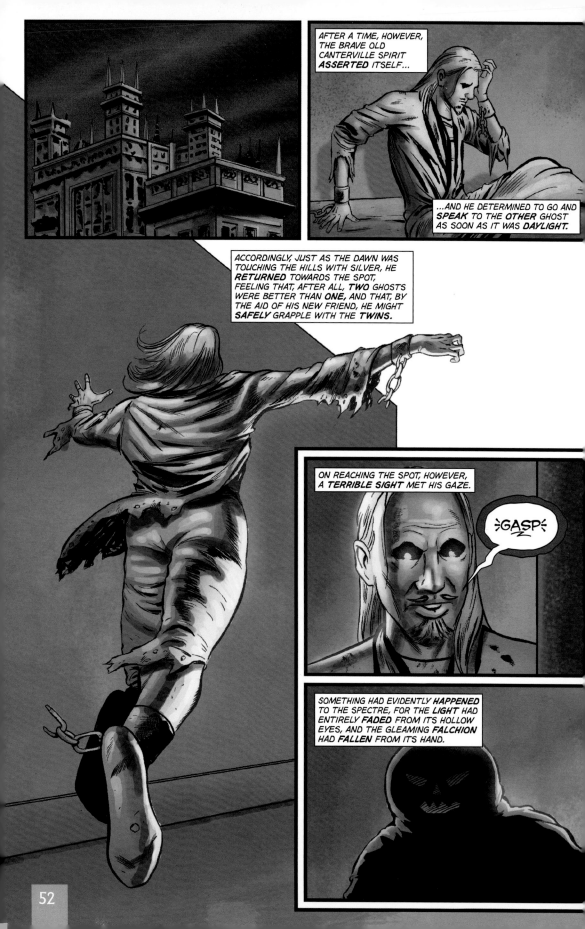

AFTER A TIME, HOWEVER, THE BRAVE OLD CANTERVILLE SPIRIT *ASSERTED* ITSELF...

...AND HE DETERMINED TO GO AND *SPEAK* TO THE *OTHER* GHOST AS SOON AS IT WAS *DAYLIGHT*.

ACCORDINGLY, JUST AS THE DAWN WAS TOUCHING THE HILLS WITH SILVER, HE *RETURNED* TOWARDS THE SPOT, FEELING THAT, AFTER ALL, *TWO* GHOSTS WERE BETTER THAN *ONE*, AND THAT, BY THE AID OF HIS NEW FRIEND, HE MIGHT *SAFELY* GRAPPLE WITH THE *TWINS*.

ON REACHING THE SPOT, HOWEVER, A *TERRIBLE SIGHT* MET HIS GAZE.

≷GASP≶

SOMETHING HAD EVIDENTLY *HAPPENED* TO THE SPECTRE, FOR THE *LIGHT* HAD ENTIRELY *FADED* FROM ITS HOLLOW EYES, AND THE GLEAMING *FALCHION* HAD *FALLEN* FROM ITS HAND.

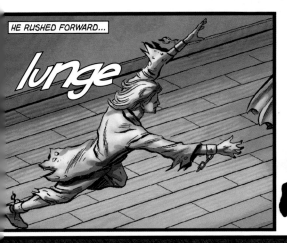

THE WHOLE THING FLASHED ACROSS HIM. HE HAD BEEN TRICKED, FOILED, AND *OUTWITTED!*

THE OLD CANTERVILLE LOOK CAME INTO HIS EYES.

HE *SWORE,* ACCORDING TO THE PICTURESQUE PHRASEOLOGY OF THE *ANTIQUE* SCHOOL, THAT, WHEN CHANTICLEER HAD SOUNDED *TWICE* HIS MERRY HORN, DEEDS OF *BLOOD* WOULD BE WROUGHT, AND *MURDER* WALK ABROAD WITH SILENT FEET.

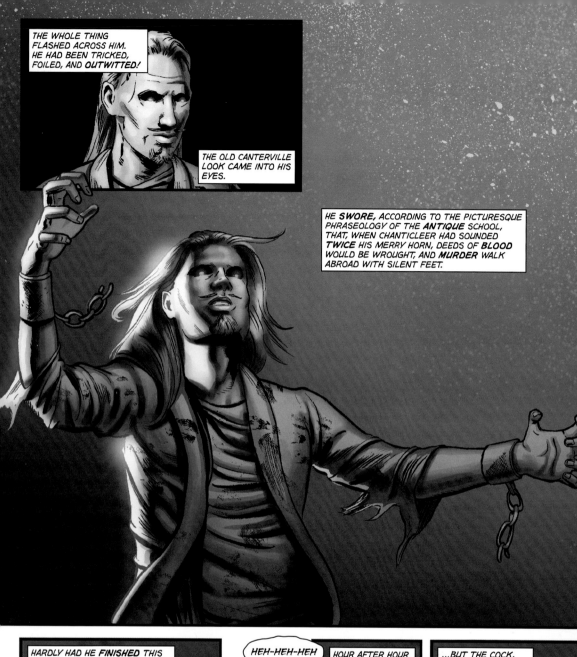

HARDLY HAD HE *FINISHED* THIS AWFUL *OATH* WHEN A COCK *CREW.*

COCK·A·DOODLE·DOO

HEH-HEH-HEH

HOUR AFTER HOUR HE *WAITED...*

...BUT THE COCK, FOR SOME *STRANGE* REASON, DID *NOT* CROW *AGAIN.*

FINALLY, AT HALF-PAST SEVEN, THE ARRIVAL OF THE *HOUSEMAIDS* MADE HIM GIVE UP HIS FEARFUL *VIGIL,* AND HE STALKED *BACK* TO HIS *ROOM,* THINKING OF HIS *VAIN* HOPE AND *BAFFLED* PURPOSE.

THERE HE CONSULTED HIS *BOOKS* OF *ANCIENT CHIVALRY*, OF WHICH HE WAS EXCEEDINGLY *FOND*, AND FOUND THAT, ON *EVERY OCCASION* ON WHICH HIS *OATH* HAD BEEN USED, CHANTICLEER HAD *ALWAYS* CROWED A *SECOND TIME*.

PERDITION *SEIZE* THE NAUGHTY FOWL.

I HAVE *SEEN* THE DAY WHEN, WITH MY STOUT *SPEAR*, I WOULD HAVE RUN HIM THROUGH THE *GORGE*, AND MADE HIM *CROW* FOR ME AN 'TWERE IN *DEATH!*

HE THEN *RETIRED* TO A COMFORTABLE *LEAD COFFIN...*

...AND *STAYED* THERE TILL *EVENING.*

CHAPTER IV

THE NEXT DAY THE GHOST WAS VERY **WEAK** AND TIRED. THE TERRIBLE **EXCITEMENT** OF THE LAST FOUR WEEKS WAS BEGINNING TO HAVE ITS **EFFECT**.

HIS **NERVES** WERE COMPLETELY **SHATTERED**, AND HE **STARTED** AT THE SLIGHTEST **NOISE**.

FOR FIVE DAYS HE **KEPT** HIS **ROOM**, AND AT LAST MADE UP HIS MIND TO **GIVE UP** THE POINT OF THE **BLOOD-STAIN** ON THE LIBRARY FLOOR. IF THE OTIS FAMILY DID NOT **WANT** IT, THEY CLEARLY DID NOT **DESERVE** IT.

THEY ARE EVIDENTLY PEOPLE ON A **LOW**, MATERIAL PLANE OF EXISTENCE, AND QUITE **INCAPABLE** OF APPRECIATING THE SYMBOLIC **VALUE** OF **SENSUOUS** PHENOMENA.

HOWEVER, IT WAS HIS SOLEMN **DUTY** TO **APPEAR** IN THE CORRIDOR ONCE A **WEEK**, AND TO **GIBBER** FROM THE LARGE ORIEL WINDOW ON THE **FIRST** AND **THIRD** WEDNESDAY IN EVERY **MONTH**, AND HE DID NOT SEE HOW HE COULD HONOURABLY **ESCAPE** FROM HIS **OBLIGATIONS**.

IT IS QUITE **TRUE** THAT HIS LIFE HAD BEEN VERY **EVIL**, BUT, UPON THE OTHER HAND, HE WAS MOST **CONSCIENTIOUS** IN ALL THINGS CONNECTED WITH THE **SUPERNATURAL**.

FOR THE NEXT THREE SATURDAYS, ACCORDINGLY, HE TRAVERSED THE CORRIDOR AS **USUAL** BETWEEN MIDNIGHT AND THREE O'CLOCK...

...TAKING EVERY POSSIBLE **PRECAUTION** AGAINST BEING EITHER **HEARD** OR **SEEN**.

HE WAS CAREFUL TO USE THE *RISING SUN LUBRICATOR* FOR OILING HIS *CHAINS.*

HE HAD *TAKEN* THIS ONE NIGHT, WHILE THE FAMILY WERE AT DINNER, BY *SLIPPING* INTO MR. OTIS'S *BEDROOM.*

HE FELT A LITTLE *HUMILIATED* AT FIRST, BUT AFTERWARDS WAS *SENSIBLE* ENOUGH TO SEE THAT THERE WAS A GREAT DEAL TO BE SAID *FOR* THE *INVENTION*, AND, TO A CERTAIN DEGREE, IT SERVED HIS PURPOSE.

STILL, IN SPITE OF *EVERYTHING*, HE WAS *NOT* LEFT *UNMOLESTED. STRINGS* WERE CONTINUALLY BEING *STRETCHED* ACROSS THE CORRIDOR...

twang

...AND ON ONE OCCASION, WHILE DRESSED FOR THE PART OF "*BLACK ISAAC*, OR THE *HUNTSMAN* OF *HOGLEY WOODS*"...

woOsh

...HE MET WITH A SEVERE *FALL*, THROUGH TREADING ON A *BUTTER-SLIDE*, WHICH THE TWINS HAD CONSTRUCTED.

57

THIS *LAST* INSULT SO *ENRAGED* HIM, THAT HE RESOLVED TO MAKE ONE *FINAL* EFFORT TO ASSERT HIS *DIGNITY* AND SOCIAL *POSITION...*

...AND DETERMINED TO *VISIT* THE INSOLENT YOUNG *ETONIANS* THE NEXT NIGHT...

...IN HIS CELEBRATED CHARACTER OF "*RECKLESS RUPERT,* OR THE *HEADLESS EARL*".

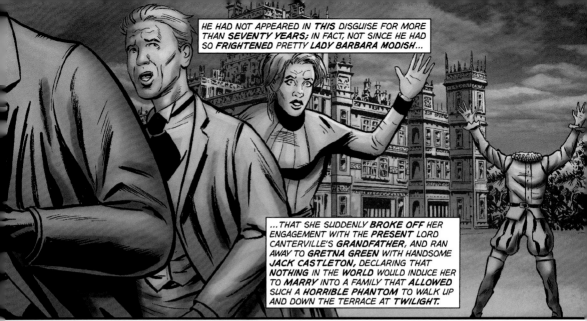

HE HAD NOT APPEARED IN *THIS* DISGUISE FOR MORE THAN *SEVENTY YEARS;* IN FACT, NOT SINCE HE HAD SO *FRIGHTENED* PRETTY *LADY BARBARA MODISH...*

...THAT SHE SUDDENLY *BROKE OFF* HER ENGAGEMENT WITH THE *PRESENT* LORD CANTERVILLE'S *GRANDFATHER,* AND RAN AWAY TO *GRETNA GREEN* WITH HANDSOME *JACK CASTLETON,* DECLARING THAT *NOTHING* IN THE *WORLD* WOULD INDUCE HER TO *MARRY* INTO A FAMILY THAT *ALLOWED* SUCH A *HORRIBLE PHANTOM* TO WALK UP AND DOWN THE TERRACE AT *TWILIGHT.*

POOR JACK WAS AFTERWARDS *SHOT* IN A *DUEL* BY LORD CANTERVILLE ON *WANDSWORTH COMMON...*

...AND LADY BARBARA *DIED* OF A *BROKEN HEART* AT TUNBRIDGE WELLS BEFORE THE YEAR WAS *OUT...*

...SO, IN *EVERY WAY,* IT HAD BEEN A *GREAT SUCCESS.*

IT TOOK HIM FULLY *THREE HOURS* TO MAKE HIS *PREPARATIONS.*

AT LAST, EVERYTHING WAS READY, AND HE WAS *PLEASED* WITH HIS *APPEARANCE*.

AT A QUARTER-PAST ONE, HE *GLIDED* OUT OF THE WAINSCOTING AND *CREPT* DOWN THE CORRIDOR.

ON *REACHING* THE ROOM OCCUPIED BY THE *TWINS*, HE FOUND THE *DOOR* JUST AJAR.

WISHING TO MAKE AN EFFECTIVE *ENTRANCE*, HE *FLUNG* IT WIDE OPEN...

⋝GASP⋜

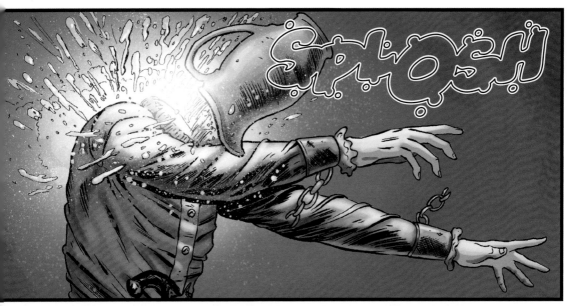

THE **SHOCK** TO HIS NERVOUS SYSTEM WAS SO **GREAT** THAT HE **FLED** BACK TO HIS **ROOM** AS HARD AS HE COULD GO.

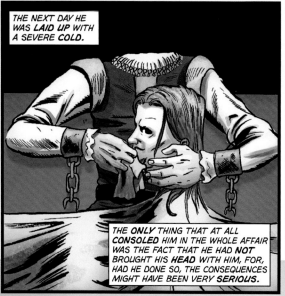

THE NEXT DAY HE WAS **LAID UP** WITH A SEVERE **COLD.**

THE **ONLY** THING THAT AT ALL **CONSOLED** HIM IN THE WHOLE AFFAIR WAS THE FACT THAT HE HAD **NOT** BROUGHT HIS **HEAD** WITH HIM, FOR, HAD HE DONE SO, THE CONSEQUENCES MIGHT HAVE BEEN VERY **SERIOUS.**

HE NOW GAVE UP **ALL** HOPE OF **EVER** FRIGHTENING THIS **RUDE** AMERICAN FAMILY...

...AND CONTENTED HIMSELF, AS A RULE, WITH **CREEPING** ABOUT THE PASSAGES.

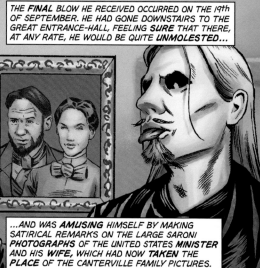

THE **FINAL** BLOW HE RECEIVED OCCURRED ON THE 19th OF SEPTEMBER. HE HAD GONE DOWNSTAIRS TO THE GREAT ENTRANCE-HALL, FEELING **SURE** THAT THERE, AT ANY RATE, HE WOULD BE QUITE **UNMOLESTED...**

...AND WAS **AMUSING** HIMSELF BY MAKING SATIRICAL REMARKS ON THE LARGE SARONI **PHOTOGRAPHS** OF THE UNITED STATES **MINISTER** AND HIS **WIFE,** WHICH HAD NOW **TAKEN** THE **PLACE** OF THE CANTERVILLE FAMILY PICTURES.

HE WAS DRESSED FOR THE CHARACTER OF "**JONAS THE GRAVELESS,** OR THE **CORPSE-SNATCHER OF CHERTSEY BARN**", ONE OF HIS MOST **REMARKABLE** IMPERSONATIONS...

...AND ONE WHICH THE CANTERVILLES HAD **EVERY** REASON TO **REMEMBER,** AS IT WAS THE **REAL** ORIGIN OF THEIR QUARREL WITH THEIR NEIGHBOUR, LORD **RUFFORD.**

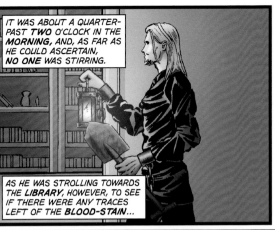

IT WAS ABOUT A QUARTER-PAST *TWO* O'CLOCK IN THE *MORNING,* AND, AS FAR AS HE COULD ASCERTAIN, *NO ONE* WAS STIRRING.

AS HE WAS STROLLING TOWARDS THE *LIBRARY,* HOWEVER, TO SEE IF THERE WERE ANY TRACES LEFT OF THE *BLOOD-STAIN...*

...SUDDENLY...

BOO!

ARGH!

SEIZED WITH A *PANIC,* WHICH, UNDER THE CIRCUMSTANCES, WAS ONLY NATURAL, HE *RUSHED* FOR THE *STAIRCASE...*

...BUT FOUND WASHINGTON OTIS *WAITING* FOR HIM THERE WITH THE BIG *GARDEN-SYRINGE.*

ARRGH!

BEING THUS *HEMMED IN* BY HIS *ENEMIES* ON EVERY SIDE...

...AND DRIVEN ALMOST TO *BAY...*

ARRRRGH!!

63

...HE VANISHED INTO THE GREAT IRON *STOVE*...

...WHICH, *FORTUNATELY* FOR HIM, WAS NOT *LIT.*

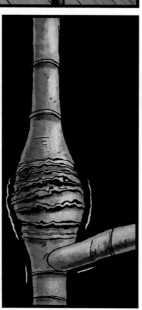

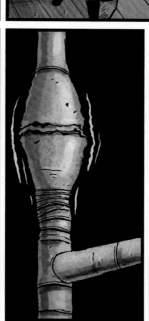

HE *ARRIVED* AT HIS OWN ROOM
IN A *TERRIBLE STATE* OF DIRT,
DISORDER, AND *DESPAIR.*

AFTER THIS HE WAS NOT SEEN *AGAIN* ON ANY *NOCTURNAL EXPEDITION.*

THE *TWINS* LAY IN *WAIT* FOR HIM ON *SEVERAL* OCCASIONS, AND *STREWED* THE PASSAGES WITH *NUTSHELLS* EVERY NIGHT...

...TO THE GREAT *ANNOYANCE* OF THEIR PARENTS AND THE SERVANTS...

...BUT IT WAS OF *NO AVAIL.* IT WAS *QUITE* EVIDENT THAT HIS *FEELINGS* WERE SO *WOUNDED* THAT HE WOULD *NOT* APPEAR.

MR. OTIS CONSEQUENTLY *RESUMED* HIS GREAT *WORK* ON THE HISTORY OF THE DEMOCRATIC PARTY, ON WHICH HE HAD BEEN ENGAGED FOR SOME *YEARS;*

MRS. OTIS ORGANISED A WONDERFUL *CLAM-BAKE,* WHICH *AMAZED* THE WHOLE *COUNTY;*

THE BOYS TOOK TO *LACROSSE, EUCHRE, POKER,* AND OTHER *AMERICAN* NATIONAL GAMES;

AND *VIRGINIA* RODE ABOUT THE LANES ON HER *PONY*, ACCOMPANIED BY THE YOUNG *DUKE OF CHESHIRE*, WHO HAD COME TO SPEND THE LAST WEEK OF HIS *HOLIDAYS* AT CANTERVILLE CHASE.

IT WAS GENERALLY *ASSUMED* THAT THE *GHOST* HAD GONE *AWAY*, AND, IN FACT, MR. OTIS WROTE A *LETTER* TO THAT EFFECT TO *LORD CANTERVILLE*...

...WHO, IN REPLY, EXPRESSED HIS GREAT *PLEASURE* AT THE NEWS, AND SENT HIS BEST *CONGRATULATIONS* TO THE MINISTER'S WORTHY WIFE.

THE OTISES, HOWEVER, WERE *DECEIVED*, FOR THE *GHOST* WAS STILL IN THE *HOUSE*, AND THOUGH NOW ALMOST AN *INVALID*, WAS BY *NO MEANS* READY TO LET MATTERS *REST*...

...PARTICULARLY AS HE HEARD THAT AMONG THE *GUESTS* WAS THE YOUNG *DUKE OF CHESHIRE*...

...WHOSE *GRAND-UNCLE*, LORD FRANCIS *STILTON*, HAD ONCE BET A HUNDRED GUINEAS WITH COLONEL CARBURY THAT HE WOULD PLAY *DICE* WITH THE CANTERVILLE GHOST...

...AND WAS *FOUND* THE NEXT MORNING LYING ON THE FLOOR OF THE CARD-ROOM IN SUCH A *HELPLESS PARALYTIC STATE,* THAT THOUGH HE LIVED ON TO A *GREAT* AGE, HE WAS NEVER ABLE TO SAY *ANYTHING* AGAIN BUT:

Double Sixes...

DOUBLE SIXES...

Double Sixes...

THE GHOST, THEN, WAS NATURALLY VERY *ANXIOUS* TO SHOW THAT HE HAD NOT *LOST* HIS *INFLUENCE* OVER THE *STILTONS,* WITH WHOM, INDEED, HE WAS *DISTANTLY CONNECTED...*

...HIS OWN FIRST COUSIN HAVING BEEN MARRIED *EN SECONDES NOCES* TO THE *SIEUR DE BULKELEY,* FROM WHOM, AS EVERY ONE KNOWS, THE DUKES OF CHESHIRE ARE LINEALLY *DESCENDED.*

ACCORDINGLY, HE MADE ARRANGEMENTS FOR *APPEARING* TO VIRGINIA'S LITTLE LOVER IN HIS *CELEBRATED* IMPERSONATION OF *"THE VAMPIRE MONK,* OR, *THE BLOODLESS BENEDICTINE"...*

AT THE LAST MOMENT, HOWEVER...

...HIS *TERROR* OF THE *TWINS* PREVENTED HIS LEAVING HIS ROOM...

...AND THE LITTLE DUKE SLEPT IN *PEACE* UNDER THE GREAT FEATHERED CANOPY IN THE ROYAL BEDCHAMBER, AND *DREAMED* OF *VIRGINIA.*

CHAPTER V

A FEW DAYS AFTER THIS, *VIRGINIA* AND HER CURLY-HAIRED *CAVALIER* WENT OUT *RIDING* ON *BROCKLEY MEADOWS*...

...WHERE SHE *TORE* HER HABIT SO *BADLY* IN GETTING THROUGH A HEDGE, THAT, ON HER RETURN HOME, SHE MADE UP HER MIND TO GO UP BY THE *BACK* STAIRCASE SO AS *NOT* TO BE *SEEN*.

AS SHE WAS RUNNING PAST THE *TAPESTRY CHAMBER*...

?

=GASP=

IT IS THE CANTERVILLE GHOST HIMSELF!

SO *FORLORN*, AND SO MUCH OUT OF *REPAIR* DID HE LOOK, THAT LITTLE VIRGINIA, WHOSE *FIRST* IDEA HAD BEEN TO *RUN AWAY* AND LOCK HERSELF IN HER *ROOM*, WAS FILLED WITH *PITY*, AND DETERMINED TO TRY AND *COMFORT* HIM.

SO *LIGHT* WAS HER FOOTFALL, AND SO *DEEP* HIS *MELANCHOLY*, THAT HE WAS NOT *AWARE* OF HER PRESENCE TILL SHE *SPOKE* TO HIM.

I AM SO *SORRY* FOR YOU.

BUT MY *BROTHERS* ARE GOING BACK TO *ETON* TO-MORROW, AND THEN, IF YOU *BEHAVE* YOURSELF, NO ONE WILL *ANNOY* YOU.

!!!

IT IS *ABSURD* ASKING *ME* TO *BEHAVE* MYSELF, --

-- *QUITE* ABSURD. I *MUST* RATTLE MY CHAINS, AND *GROAN* THROUGH KEYHOLES, AND WALK ABOUT AT *NIGHT,* IF *THAT* IS WHAT YOU MEAN.

IT IS MY *ONLY* REASON FOR *EXISTING.*

IT IS *NO* REASON AT *ALL* FOR EXISTING, AND YOU *KNOW* YOU HAVE BEEN *VERY* WICKED.

MRS. UMNEY *TOLD* US, THE FIRST DAY WE ARRIVED HERE, THAT YOU HAD *KILLED* YOUR *WIFE.*

WELL, I QUITE *ADMIT* IT, BUT IT WAS A PURELY *FAMILY* MATTER, AND CONCERNED *NO ONE* ELSE.

72

-- AND AS FOR DISHONESTY, YOU KNOW YOU STOLE THE PAINTS OUT OF MY BOX TO TRY AND FURBISH UP THAT RIDICULOUS BLOOD-STAIN IN THE LIBRARY.

FIRST YOU TOOK ALL MY REDS, INCLUDING THE VERMILION, AND I COULDN'T DO ANY MORE SUNSETS, --

-- THEN YOU TOOK THE EMERALD-GREEN AND THE CHROME-YELLOW, --

-- AND FINALLY I HAD NOTHING LEFT BUT INDIGO AND CHINESE WHITE, AND COULD ONLY DO MOONLIGHT SCENES, --

-- WHICH ARE ALWAYS DEPRESSING TO LOOK AT, AND NOT AT ALL EASY TO PAINT.

I NEVER TOLD ON YOU, THOUGH I WAS VERY MUCH ANNOYED, AND IT WAS MOST RIDICULOUS, THE WHOLE THING; FOR WHO EVER HEARD OF EMERALD-GREEN BLOOD?

WELL, *REALLY*, WHAT WAS I TO *DO?* IT IS A VERY *DIFFICULT* THING TO GET *REAL* BLOOD NOWADAYS,

AND, AS YOUR BROTHER *BEGAN* IT ALL WITH HIS *PARAGON DETERGENT*, I CERTAINLY SAW *NO* REASON WHY *I* SHOULD NOT HAVE YOUR *PAINTS.*

AS FOR *COLOUR*, THAT IS *ALWAYS* A MATTER OF *TASTE*: THE *CANTERVILLES* HAVE *BLUE* BLOOD, FOR INSTANCE, THE VERY *BLUEST* IN *ENGLAND;*

BUT I KNOW YOU *AMERICANS* DON'T *CARE* FOR THINGS OF *THIS* KIND.

YOU KNOW *NOTHING* ABOUT IT, AND THE BEST THING *YOU* CAN DO IS TO *EMIGRATE* AND *IMPROVE* YOUR *MIND.*

MY FATHER WILL BE ONLY TOO *HAPPY* TO GIVE YOU A FREE *PASSAGE*,

AND THOUGH THERE IS A HEAVY DUTY ON *SPIRITS* OF EVERY KIND,

THERE WILL BE *NO* DIFFICULTY ABOUT THE *CUSTOM* HOUSE, AS THE OFFICERS ARE ALL *DEMOCRATS.*

ONCE IN *NEW YORK*, YOU ARE *SURE* TO BE A *GREAT* SUCCESS.

I KNOW *LOTS* OF PEOPLE THERE WHO WOULD GIVE A HUNDRED THOUSAND DOLLARS TO HAVE A GRANDFATHER, AND MUCH *MORE* THAN THAT TO HAVE A FAMILY *GHOST.*

FAR AWAY BEYOND THE PINE-WOODS, THERE IS A LITTLE *GARDEN*.

THERE THE GRASS GROWS *LONG* AND *DEEP*, THERE ARE THE GREAT WHITE *STARS* OF THE HEMLOCK FLOWER, THERE THE NIGHTINGALE *SINGS* ALL NIGHT LONG.

ALL NIGHT LONG HE *SINGS*, AND THE COLD, CRYSTAL MOON LOOKS *DOWN*, AND THE YEW-TREE SPREADS OUT ITS GIANT *ARMS* OVER THE *SLEEPERS*.

You mean the Garden of *Death*.

YES, *DEATH*. DEATH MUST BE SO *BEAUTIFUL*. TO LIE IN THE SOFT BROWN *EARTH*, WITH THE GRASSES WAVING ABOVE ONE'S HEAD, AND LISTEN TO *SILENCE*.

TO HAVE NO *YESTERDAY*, AND NO *TO-MORROW*. TO FORGET TIME; TO FORGET LIFE, TO BE AT *PEACE*.

YOU CAN HELP ME. YOU CAN *OPEN* FOR ME THE *PORTALS* OF *DEATH'S* HOUSE, FOR LOVE IS ALWAYS *WITH* YOU, AND LOVE IS *STRONGER* THAN DEATH IS.

HAVE YOU EVER READ THE OLD *PROPHECY* ON THE LIBRARY WINDOW?

OH, **OFTEN**; I KNOW IT QUITE WELL. IT IS PAINTED IN **CURIOUS** BLACK LETTERS, AND IT IS **DIFFICULT** TO READ.

THERE ARE ONLY SIX LINES:

When a golden girl can win
Prayer from out the lips of sin,
When the barren almond bears,
And a little child gives away its tears,
Then shall all the house be still
And peace come to Canterville.

BUT I DON'T KNOW WHAT THEY **MEAN**.

THEY MEAN, THAT YOU MUST **WEEP** WITH ME FOR MY SINS, BECAUSE I HAVE NO **TEARS**, AND **PRAY** WITH ME FOR MY SOUL, BECAUSE I HAVE NO **FAITH**,

AND **THEN**, IF YOU HAVE ALWAYS BEEN **SWEET**, AND **GOOD**, AND **GENTLE**,

THE ANGEL OF **DEATH** WILL HAVE **MERCY** ON ME.

YOU WILL SEE **FEARFUL** SHAPES IN DARKNESS, AND WICKED **VOICES** WILL WHISPER IN YOUR **EAR**, BUT THEY WILL NOT **HARM** YOU, FOR AGAINST THE **PURITY** OF A LITTLE CHILD THE POWERS OF **HELL** CANNOT **PREVAIL**.

VIRGINIA MADE NO *ANSWER*, AND THE *GHOST* WRUNG HIS *HANDS* IN WILD *DESPAIR*.

SUDDENLY...

I AM NOT *AFRAID*, AND I WILL ASK THE ANGEL TO HAVE *MERCY* ON YOU.

OH!

≠xXx≠

HIS *FINGERS* WERE AS *COLD* AS *ICE*, AND HIS LIPS *BURNED* LIKE FIRE...

81

...BUT VIRGINIA DID NOT *FALTER,* AS HE *LED* HER ACROSS THE DUSKY *ROOM.*

ON THE FADED GREEN *TAPESTRY* WERE BROIDERED LITTLE HUNTSMEN. THEY *BLEW* THEIR TASSELLED *HORNS* AND WITH THEIR TINY *HANDS* WAVED TO HER TO *GO BACK...*

GO BACK!

LITTLE VIRGINIA, GO BACK!

...BUT THE *GHOST* CLUTCHED HER *HAND* MORE TIGHTLY...

...AND SHE *SHUT* HER EYES *AGAINST* THEM.

HORRIBLE *ANIMALS* BLINKED AT HER FROM THE *CHIMNEY-PIECE.*

BEWARE!

LITTLE VIRGINIA, BEWARE, WE MAY NEVER SEE YOU AGAIN!

HE MUTTERED SOME **WORDS** SHE COULD **NOT** UNDERSTAND.

SHE OPENED HER EYES, AND SAW THE **WALL** SLOWLY **FADING AWAY.**

QUICK, **QUICK,** OR IT WILL BE TOO **LATE.**

83

IN A **MOMENT**, THE WAINSCOTING HAD **CLOSED** BEHIND THEM, AND THE TAPESTRY CHAMBER WAS **EMPTY**.

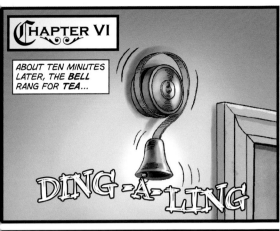

CHAPTER VI

ABOUT TEN MINUTES LATER, THE **BELL** RANG FOR **TEA**...

DING-A-LING

AS VIRGINIA DID NOT COME **DOWN,** MRS. OTIS SENT UP ONE OF THE FOOTMEN TO TELL HER.

AFTER A LITTLE TIME...

I COULD NOT **FIND** MISS VIRGINIA **ANYWHERE.**

AS SHE WAS IN THE **HABIT** OF GOING OUT TO THE **GARDEN** EVERY EVENING TO GET **FLOWERS** FOR THE DINNER-TABLE, MRS. OTIS WAS **NOT** AT ALL **ALARMED** AT FIRST...

...BUT WHEN SIX O'CLOCK STRUCK, AND VIRGINIA DID **NOT** APPEAR, SHE BECAME REALLY **AGITATED**...

...AND SENT THE **BOYS** OUT TO **LOOK** FOR HER...

...WHILE SHE HERSELF AND MR. OTIS SEARCHED **EVERY** ROOM IN THE **HOUSE.**

AT HALF-PAST SIX THE BOYS CAME BACK AND SAID THAT THEY COULD FIND **NO TRACE** OF HER **ANYWHERE**.

MR. OTIS SUDDENLY **REMEMBERED** THAT, SOME DAYS BEFORE, HE HAD GIVEN A BAND OF **GYPSIES** PERMISSION TO CAMP IN THE PARK.

HE ACCORDINGLY AT **ONCE** SET OFF FOR **BLACKFELL HOLLOW**, WHERE HE KNEW THEY WERE, ACCOMPANIED BY HIS ELDEST SON AND TWO OF THE FARM-SERVANTS.

THE LITTLE DUKE OF CHESHIRE, WHO WAS PERFECTLY **FRANTIC** WITH ANXIETY, **BEGGED HARD** TO BE ALLOWED TO GO TOO, BUT MR. OTIS WOULD NOT ALLOW HIM, AS HE WAS AFRAID THERE MIGHT BE A **SCUFFLE**.

ON *ARRIVING* AT THE SPOT, HOWEVER, HE FOUND THAT THE GYPSIES HAD *GONE*, AND IT WAS EVIDENT THAT THEIR DEPARTURE HAD BEEN RATHER *SUDDEN*.

HAVING SENT OFF *WASHINGTON* AND THE TWO MEN TO *SCOUR* THE DISTRICT, HE RAN *HOME*, AND DESPATCHED *TELEGRAMS* TO ALL THE POLICE INSPECTORS IN THE *COUNTY*...

...TELLING THEM TO LOOK OUT FOR A LITTLE GIRL WHO HAD BEEN *KIDNAPPED* BY TRAMPS OR GYPSIES.

HE THEN ORDERED HIS HORSE TO BE BROUGHT ROUND, AND, AFTER *INSISTING* ON HIS WIFE AND THE THREE BOYS SITTING DOWN TO *DINNER*, RODE OFF DOWN THE *ASCOT ROAD.*

HE HAD *HARDLY*, HOWEVER, GONE A *COUPLE* OF *MILES* WHEN...

clip clop
clip clop

I'M AWFULLY **SORRY**, MR. OTIS, BUT I **CAN'T** EAT ANY DINNER AS LONG AS VIRGINIA IS **LOST**.

PLEASE, DON'T BE **ANGRY** WITH ME; IF YOU HAD **LET** US BE ENGAGED LAST YEAR, THERE WOULD NEVER HAVE **BEEN** ALL THIS **TROUBLE**.

YOU **WON'T** SEND ME **BACK**, WILL YOU?

I **CAN'T** GO!

I **WON'T** GO!

WELL, CECIL, IF YOU **WON'T** GO BACK I SUPPOSE YOU **MUST** COME WITH ME,

BUT I MUST GET YOU A **HAT** AT ASCOT.

OH, *BOTHER MY HAT!* I WANT *VIRGINIA!*

THEY GALLOPED ON TO THE RAILWAY STATION.

THERE MR. OTIS INQUIRED OF THE STATION-MASTER IF ANY ONE ANSWERING TO THE DESCRIPTION OF VIRGINIA HAD BEEN **SEEN** ON THE PLATFORM, BUT COULD GET **NO** NEWS OF HER.

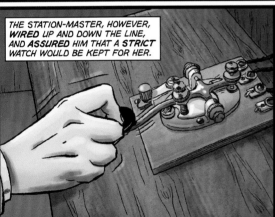

THE STATION-MASTER, HOWEVER, **WIRED** UP AND DOWN THE LINE, AND **ASSURED** HIM THAT A **STRICT** WATCH WOULD BE KEPT FOR HER.

AFTER HAVING BOUGHT A **HAT** FOR THE LITTLE DUKE...

...MR. OTIS RODE OFF TO **BEXLEY,** A VILLAGE ABOUT FOUR MILES AWAY, WHICH HE WAS TOLD WAS A WELL-KNOWN HAUNT OF THE **GYPSIES,** AS THERE WAS A LARGE COMMON NEXT TO IT.

HERE THEY ROUSED UP THE RURAL *POLICEMAN*, BUT COULD GET NO *INFORMATION* FROM HIM...

...AND, AFTER RIDING *ALL OVER* THE COMMON...

...THEY TURNED THEIR HORSES' HEADS *HOMEWARDS*...

...AND REACHED THE CHASE ABOUT ELEVEN O'CLOCK, DEAD-TIRED AND ALMOST *HEART-BROKEN.*

THEY FOUND **WASHINGTON** AND THE **TWINS** WAITING FOR THEM AT THE GATE-HOUSE WITH LANTERNS.

WE HAVEN'T DISCOVERED EVEN THE SLIGHTEST **TRACE** OF **VIRGINIA.**

WE **CAUGHT** THE **GYPSIES** ON BROCKLEY MEADOWS, BUT SHE WAS **NOT** WITH THEM.

THEY EXPLAINED THEIR **SUDDEN** DEPARTURE BY SAYING THAT THEY HAD **MISTAKEN** THE DATE OF **CHORTON FAIR,** AND HAD GONE OFF IN A HURRY FOR FEAR THEY SHOULD BE **LATE.**

INDEED, THEY HAD BEEN QUITE **DISTRESSED** AT HEARING OF VIRGINIA'S DISAPPEARANCE, AS THEY WERE VERY **GRATEFUL** TO MR. OTIS FOR HAVING ALLOWED THEM TO **CAMP** IN HIS PARK, AND **FOUR** OF THEIR NUMBER HAD STAYED BEHIND TO **HELP** IN THE SEARCH.

THE **CARP-POND** HAD BEEN **DRAGGED,** AND THE WHOLE CHASE **THOROUGHLY** GONE OVER, BUT WITHOUT ANY **RESULT.**

IT WAS EVIDENT THAT, FOR **THAT** NIGHT AT ANY RATE, VIRGINIA WAS **LOST** TO THEM;

AND IT WAS IN A **STATE** OF THE DEEPEST **DEPRESSION** THAT MR. OTIS AND THE BOYS **WALKED** UP TO THE **HOUSE.**

THE **SERVANTS** WERE FRIGHTENED...

...AND POOR MRS. OTIS WAS ALMOST OUT OF HER MIND WITH **TERROR** AND **ANXIETY.** SHE WAS HAVING HER FOREHEAD **BATHED** WITH EAU-DE-COLOGNE BY THE OLD HOUSEKEEPER.

MR. OTIS AT ONCE **INSISTED** ON HER HAVING SOMETHING TO **EAT,** AND ORDERED UP **SUPPER** FOR THE WHOLE PARTY.

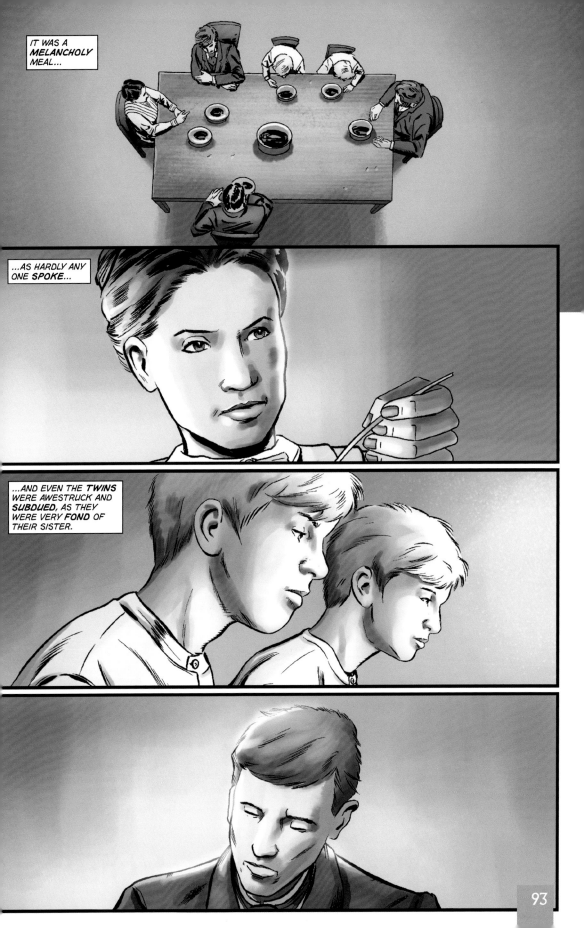

IT WAS A *MELANCHOLY* MEAL...

...AS HARDLY ANY ONE *SPOKE*...

...AND EVEN THE *TWINS* WERE AWESTRUCK AND *SUBDUED*, AS THEY WERE VERY *FOND* OF THEIR SISTER.

WHEN THEY HAD FINISHED, MR. OTIS, IN *SPITE* OF THE *ENTREATIES* OF THE LITTLE *DUKE*, ORDERED THEM ALL TO *BED*, SAYING THAT NOTHING *MORE* COULD BE DONE THAT NIGHT...

...AND THAT HE WOULD TELEGRAPH IN THE MORNING TO *SCOTLAND YARD* FOR SOME *DETECTIVES* TO BE SENT DOWN *IMMEDIATELY*.

MIDNIGHT...

BONG!

CRAAASH! SHRIEEEEK!

BRRRUUUUHHHHH

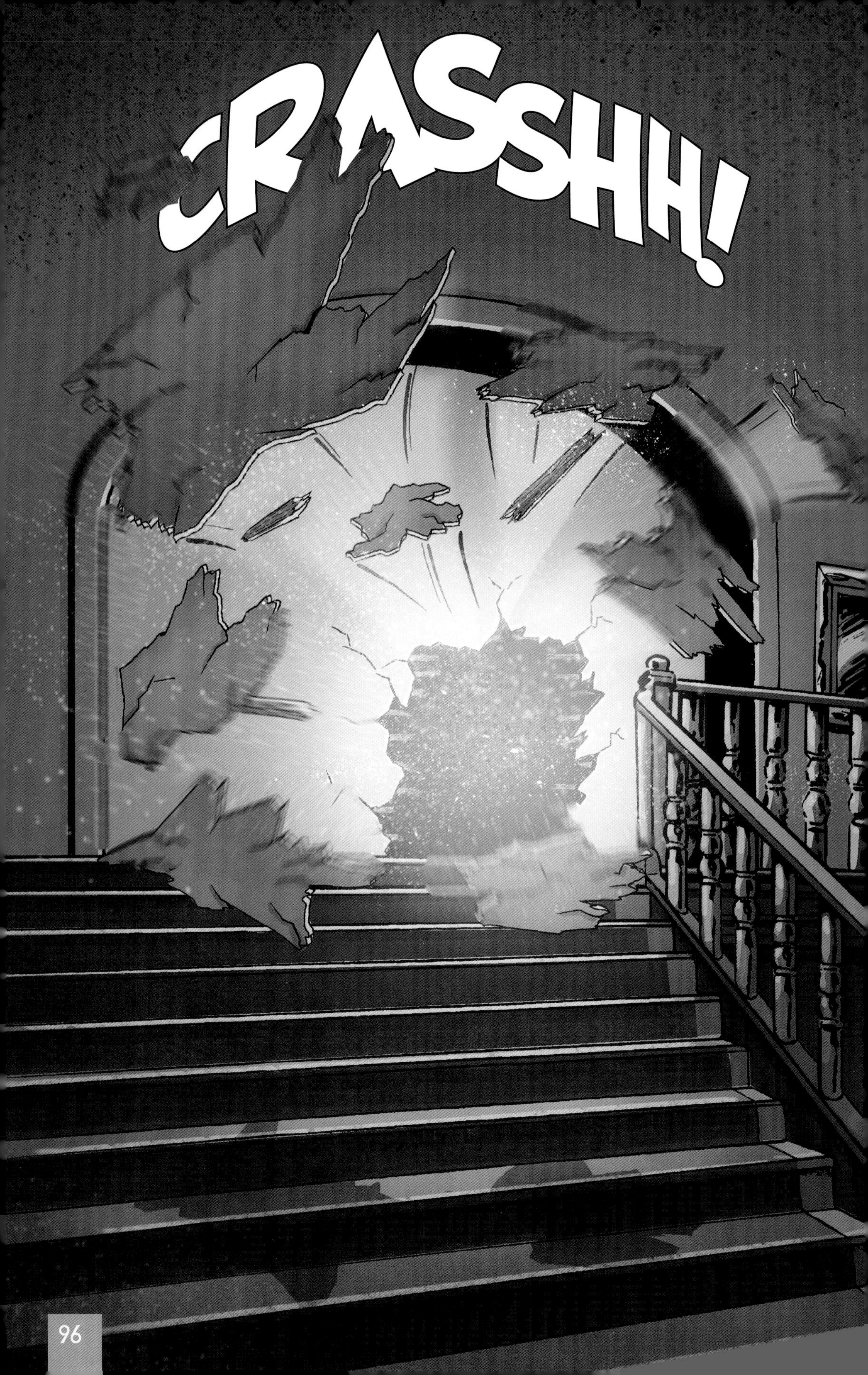
CRASSHH!

≈GASP≈

?!?

OUT ON THE **LANDING**, LOOKING VERY **PALE** AND **WHITE**, WITH A LITTLE **CASKET** IN HER HAND...

...STEPPED VIRGINIA.

THE WHOLE FAMILY *GAZED* AT HER IN MUTE *AMAZEMENT*, BUT SHE WAS QUITE *GRAVE* AND *SERIOUS*.

TURNING ROUND, SHE *LED* THEM THROUGH THE *OPENING* IN THE WAINSCOTING...

...DOWN A NARROW *SECRET* CORRIDOR.

FINALLY, THEY CAME TO A GREAT OAK *DOOR*, STUDDED WITH *RUSTY NAILS.*

WHEN VIRGINIA *TOUCHED* IT, IT *SWUNG BACK* ON ITS HEAVY HINGES...

CREEEEAAAK!

IMBEDDED IN THE **WALL** WAS A HUGE **IRON RING**, AND **CHAINED** TO IT WAS A GAUNT **SKELETON**, THAT WAS **STRETCHED** OUT AT **FULL LENGTH** ON THE STONE FLOOR, AND SEEMED TO BE **TRYING** TO **GRASP** WITH ITS LONG FLESHLESS FINGERS AN OLD-FASHIONED **TRENCHER** AND **EWER**, THAT WERE PLACED JUST **OUT** OF ITS **REACH**.

THE **JUG** HAD EVIDENTLY BEEN ONCE **FILLED** WITH **WATER**, AS IT WAS COVERED INSIDE WITH GREEN **MOULD**.

THERE WAS **NOTHING** ON THE **TRENCHER** BUT A PILE OF **DUST**.

squeak

VIRGINIA BEGAN TO *PRAY* SILENTLY, WHILE THE *REST* OF THE PARTY LOOKED ON IN *WONDER* AT THE *TERRIBLE TRAGEDY* WHOSE *SECRET* WAS NOW *DISCLOSED* TO THEM.

≒GASP≒

ONE OF THE *TWINS* LOOKED OUT OF THE *WINDOW* TO TRY AND DISCOVER IN WHAT *WING* OF THE HOUSE THE *ROOM* WAS SITUATED.

HALLO!

CHAPTER VII

FOUR DAYS AFTER THESE *CURIOUS* INCIDENTS, A *FUNERAL* STARTED FROM CANTERVILLE CHASE AT ABOUT ELEVEN O'CLOCK AT NIGHT.

LORD *CANTERVILLE* WAS THE *CHIEF MOURNER,* HAVING COME UP *SPECIALLY* FROM WALES TO ATTEND THE FUNERAL, AND SAT IN THE FIRST CARRIAGE ALONG WITH LITTLE VIRGINIA.

THEN CAME THE UNITED STATES MINISTER AND HIS WIFE, THEN WASHINGTON AND THE THREE BOYS...

...AND IN THE *LAST* CARRIAGE WAS *MRS. UMNEY.* IT WAS GENERALLY FELT THAT, AS SHE HAD BEEN *FRIGHTENED* BY THE GHOST FOR MORE THAN *FIFTY* YEARS OF HER LIFE, SHE HAD A *RIGHT* TO SEE THE *LAST* OF HIM.

A DEEP **GRAVE** HAD BEEN DUG IN THE CORNER OF THE CHURCHYARD, JUST UNDER THE OLD **YEW-TREE**...

...AND THE SERVICE WAS READ IN THE MOST **IMPRESSIVE** MANNER BY THE REV. **AUGUSTUS DAMPIER.**

WHEN THE CEREMONY WAS *OVER,* THE SERVANTS...

...ACCORDING TO AN OLD CUSTOM OBSERVED IN THE CANTERVILLE FAMILY, *EXTINGUISHED* THEIR *TORCHES...*

...AND, AS THE COFFIN WAS BEING LOWERED INTO THE GRAVE, *VIRGINIA* STEPPED *FORWARD.*

TWEET-TW-TWEET-TWEET

SHE THOUGHT OF THE GHOST'S DESCRIPTION OF THE *GARDEN* OF *DEATH* AND HER EYES BECAME DIM WITH *TEARS.*

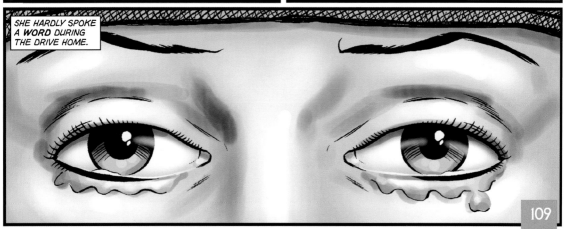

SHE HARDLY SPOKE A *WORD* DURING THE DRIVE HOME.

THE NEXT MORNING, BEFORE LORD CANTERVILLE WENT UP TO TOWN, MR. OTIS HAD AN *INTERVIEW* WITH HIM ON THE SUBJECT OF THE *JEWELS* THE *GHOST* HAD GIVEN TO *VIRGINIA*.

THEIR VALUE WAS SO *GREAT* THAT MR. OTIS FELT CONSIDERABLE *SCRUPLES* ABOUT ALLOWING HIS DAUGHTER TO *ACCEPT* THEM.

MY LORD, I KNOW THAT IN THIS COUNTRY *MORTMAIN* IS HELD TO APPLY TO *TRINKETS* AS WELL AS TO LAND, --

-- AND IT IS QUITE **CLEAR** TO ME THAT THESE **JEWELS** ARE, OR *SHOULD BE*, **HEIRLOOMS** IN YOUR FAMILY.

I MUST **BEG** YOU, ACCORDINGLY, TO TAKE THEM TO LONDON WITH YOU, AND TO REGARD THEM SIMPLY AS A PORTION OF **YOUR** PROPERTY WHICH HAS BEEN **RESTORED** TO YOU UNDER CERTAIN **STRANGE** CONDITIONS.

AS FOR MY **DAUGHTER**, SHE IS MERELY A **CHILD**, AND HAS AS YET, I AM GLAD TO SAY, BUT **LITTLE** INTEREST IN SUCH APPURTENANCES OF IDLE **LUXURY**.

I AM **ALSO** INFORMED BY MRS. OTIS, WHO, I MAY SAY, IS NO MEAN **AUTHORITY** UPON ART,

-- HAVING HAD THE PRIVILEGE OF SPENDING SEVERAL WINTERS IN **BOSTON** WHEN SHE WAS A GIRL --

THAT THESE GEMS ARE OF **GREAT MONETARY WORTH**, AND IF OFFERED FOR SALE WOULD FETCH A **TALL** PRICE.

FOR MY OWN PART, I CONFESS I AM A GOOD DEAL **SURPRISED** TO FIND A CHILD OF MINE EXPRESSING **SYMPATHY** WITH MEDIAEVALISM IN **ANY** FORM, --

-- AND CAN ONLY **ACCOUNT** FOR IT BY THE FACT THAT VIRGINIA WAS **BORN** IN ONE OF YOUR LONDON **SUBURBS** SHORTLY AFTER MRS. OTIS HAD RETURNED FROM A TRIP TO ATHENS.

MY DEAR SIR, YOUR CHARMING LITTLE DAUGHTER RENDERED MY **UNLUCKY** ANCESTOR, SIR SIMON, A VERY **IMPORTANT** SERVICE, --

-- AND I AND MY FAMILY ARE MUCH **INDEBTED** TO HER FOR HER **MARVELLOUS** COURAGE AND PLUCK.

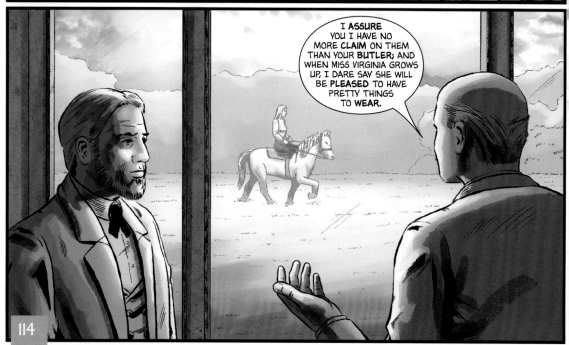

BESIDES, YOU **FORGET**, MR. OTIS, THAT **YOU** TOOK THE FURNITURE AND THE GHOST AT A VALUATION, AND **ANYTHING** THAT BELONGED TO THE GHOST PASSED AT ONCE INTO **YOUR** POSSESSION, --

-- AS, WHATEVER **ACTIVITY** SIR SIMON MAY HAVE SHOWN IN THE CORRIDOR AT NIGHT, IN POINT OF **LAW** HE WAS REALLY **DEAD**, AND YOU ACQUIRED HIS PROPERTY BY **PURCHASE**.

MR. OTIS WAS A GOOD DEAL **DISTRESSED** AT LORD CANTERVILLE'S REFUSAL, AND BEGGED HIM TO **RECONSIDER** HIS DECISION...

...BUT THE GOOD-NATURED PEER WAS QUITE **FIRM**, AND **FINALLY** INDUCED THE MINISTER TO ALLOW HIS DAUGHTER TO **RETAIN** THE PRESENT THE **GHOST** HAD **GIVEN** HER.

WHEN, IN THE SPRING OF 1890, THE YOUNG DUCHESS OF CHESHIRE WAS PRESENTED AT THE *QUEEN'S* FIRST DRAWING-ROOM ON THE OCCASION OF HER *MARRIAGE,* HER JEWELS WERE THE UNIVERSAL THEME OF *ADMIRATION.*

FOR VIRGINIA RECEIVED THE *CORONET,* WHICH IS THE REWARD OF ALL *GOOD* LITTLE AMERICAN GIRLS...

...AND WAS MARRIED TO HER BOY-LOVER AS SOON AS HE CAME OF AGE.

THEY WERE BOTH SO *CHARMING,* AND THEY *LOVED* EACH OTHER SO *MUCH,* THAT EVERY ONE WAS *DELIGHTED* AT THE MATCH, *EXCEPT* THE OLD MARCHIONESS OF DUMBLETON...

...WHO HAD TRIED TO *CATCH* THE DUKE FOR ONE OF HER *SEVEN* UNMARRIED *DAUGHTERS,* AND HAD GIVEN NO LESS THAN *THREE* EXPENSIVE DINNER-PARTIES FOR THAT PURPOSE...

...AND, *STRANGE* TO SAY, MR. OTIS *HIMSELF.* MR. OTIS WAS EXTREMELY *FOND* OF THE YOUNG DUKE PERSONALLY, BUT, THEORETICALLY, HE *OBJECTED* TO TITLES, AND, TO USE HIS OWN WORDS:

I AM NOT WITHOUT *APPREHENSION,* LEST, AMID THE ENERVATING INFLUENCES OF A PLEASURE-LOVING *ARISTOCRACY,* THE TRUE PRINCIPLES OF *REPUBLICAN* SIMPLICITY SHOULD BE FORGOTTEN.

HIS OBJECTIONS, HOWEVER, WERE COMPLETELY *OVERRULED...*

...AND I BELIEVE THAT WHEN HE WALKED UP THE AISLE OF ST. GEORGE'S, HANOVER SQUARE, WITH HIS *DAUGHTER* LEANING ON HIS *ARM...*

...THERE WAS NOT A *PROUDER* MAN IN THE WHOLE *LENGTH* AND *BREADTH* OF ENGLAND.

THE DUKE AND DUCHESS, AFTER THE HONEYMOON WAS OVER, WENT DOWN TO *CANTERVILLE CHASE,* AND ON THE DAY AFTER THEIR ARRIVAL THEY WALKED OVER IN THE AFTERNOON TO THE LONELY *CHURCHYARD* BY THE PINE-WOODS.

THERE HAD BEEN A GREAT DEAL OF *DIFFICULTY* AT FIRST ABOUT THE *INSCRIPTION* ON SIR SIMON'S *TOMBSTONE.*

AFTER THEY HAD *STOOD* BY IT FOR *SOME TIME...*

117

...THEY STROLLED INTO THE RUINED CHANCEL OF THE OLD *ABBEY*.

VIRGINIA, --

-- A WIFE SHOULD HAVE NO SECRETS FROM HER HUSBAND.

SIR SIMON
DE
CANTERVILLE
1545 - 1886

WHEN A GOLDEN GIRL CAN WIN
PRAYER FROM OUT THE LIPS OF SIN,
WHEN THE BARREN ALMOND BEARS,
AND A LITTLE CHILD GIVES AWAY ITS TEARS,
THEN SHALL ALL THE HOUSE BE STILL
AND PEACE COME TO CANTERVILLE.

The Canterville Ghost

The End

Oscar Wilde

(1854 – 1900)

O scar Fingal O'Flahertie Wills Wilde was born on 16th October 1854 in Dublin, Ireland to well-respected parents.

His father, Sir William Wilde (1815-1876), was a successful doctor who specialised in the treatment of ear and eye diseases and who was appointed medical advisor for the 1841 Irish Census. His records were so meticulous that he was appointed the assistant commissioner for the following censuses of 1851 and 1861, receiving a knighthood for his work in 1864. Twenty years earlier, in 1844, he founded St. Mark's Opthalmic Hospital, where he provided free treatment to the poor of the city. He died in 1876.

Although his father wrote books on archaeology and folklore, it was Oscar's mother, Lady Jane Francesca Wilde (1820-1896), who was undoubtedly the source of his linguistic and artistic talent. She rose to prominence writing revolutionary poems for an Irish newspaper from 1846 to 1848. She also had a good knowledge of several European languages, translating books such as the gothic horror novel *Sidonia the Sorceress* by Wilhelm Meinhold, which itself was to become an influence for the darker side of Oscar's own writing.

© National Portrait Gallery, London

"One's past is what one is. It is the only way by which people should be judged."

Oscar was the second of three children for Jane; William "Willie" Charles Kingsbury was born two years earlier in 1852, and a daughter, Isola Emily Francesca, followed in 1857. Unfortunately, Emily died of a sudden fever at the age of ten, and this affected the young Oscar who, for the rest of his life, carried a lock of her hair sealed in a decorated envelope.

A brilliant scholar, Oscar attended the Portora Royal School at Enniskillen, winning top prizes for his classical studies. He was awarded a scholarship to attend Trinity College in Dublin, where he continued to excel in the classics. This culminated in him being awarded the honour of a foundation scholarship in 1872. Two years later, in 1874, he won the college's Berkeley Gold Medal for Greek, and he was awarded a Demyship scholarship to attend Magdalen College in Oxford, England.

> "*I am so clever that sometimes I don't understand a single word of what I am saying.*"

It was while at Magdalen College, in 1878, that Wilde won the Newdigate Prize for his poem *Ravenna*. The Newdigate Prize is named after its founder, Sir Roger Newdigate (1719-1806) and the scheme is still operational today. It was also during his time at Oxford that Oscar became involved with the Aesthetic Movement (see page 130). Amongst other things, the Aesthetes promoted the idea of art as a way of life. It was a concept that Wilde embraced wholeheartedly, and he followed its ideals until the end of his life.

> "*It is through art, and through art only, that we can realise our perfection.*"

After graduating with first class honours from Oxford, Wilde went to live in Chelsea, London with his friend, Frank Miles, a popular society portrait artist. He published a collection of poetry, *Poems* (1881), and completed a tour of America and Canada (see page 131), promoting *Poems* and delivering lectures on aesthetics.

> "*I never travel without my diary. One should always have something sensational to read in the train.*"

In 1883, he arranged for his play, *Vera*, to open in New York. He attended the first night, but the play was far from a success, and it quickly folded.

He returned to England and, in 1884, married Constance Lloyd. The daughter of a barrister and also from Dublin, Constance spoke a number of languages and was well read. Interestingly, she had previously turned down an offer of marriage from the author of *Dracula*, Bram Stoker. Oscar and Constance had two sons: Cyril in 1885 and Vyvyan in 1886. Oscar now needed a steady income to support his family, and, although he was a regular contributor to a number of magazines, he decided to accept the position of editor at *Woman's World* magazine in 1887.

> "*It is better to have a permanent income than to be fascinating.*"

This was the start of Wilde's most prolific period. That same year saw him complete his short story, *The Canterville Ghost*, which was serialised in *Court and Society Review* (a magazine for the upper classes) and republished in *Lord Arthur Savile's Crime and Other Stories* in 1891. In 1888 he wrote *The Happy Prince and Other Tales,* following it with another collection of short stories in 1892, *The House of Pomegranates*. His only novel, *The Picture of Dorian Gray,* first appeared in an American magazine in 1890 and caused quite a stir amongst its Victorian readership because of its loose morals. He expanded the story, and it appeared in book form the following year.

> "*There is no such thing as a moral or an immoral book. Books are well written, or badly written.*"

Wilde had a great love for the theatre. Perhaps because of his devotion to the Aesthetic Movement, his writing and, indeed, his very way of life was always grand and theatrical.

He also possessed a sharp wit, perfect for the stage. Despite earlier theatrical failures, his play *Lady Windermere's Fan* opened to great critical acclaim in 1891.

> "*I regard the theatre as the greatest of all art forms, the most immediate way in which a human being can share with another the sense of what it is to be a human being.*"

More plays quickly followed, including *A Woman of No Importance* (1893), *An Ideal Husband* (1895) and perhaps his most famous play of all, *The Importance of Being Earnest* (1895), establishing Wilde as a leading playwright. He was not without his detractors, however. Due to his colourful attire and behaviour, he was often mocked, most notably in the comic opera *Patience*, written by Gilbert and Sullivan, which ridiculed both the Aesthetic Movement and Wilde himself.

> "*There is only one thing in life worse than being talked about, and that is not being talked about.*"

Wilde was now at the peak of his career. Popular in London society and renowned for his piercing humour, it seemed that behind this mask lay a complex man, torn between his ideals, his need to uphold respectability, and his sexuality; within this turmoil, his celebrity status and position quickly tumbled.

> "*I suppose society is wonderfully delightful. To be in it is merely a bore. But to be out of it is simply a tragedy.*"

Just as he was becoming well known as a playwright in 1891, Wilde met the poet Lord Alfred "Bosie" Douglas. Bosie, the third son of the Marquess of Queensbury, became the close companion of Wilde and, despite it being against the law at the time to have a homosexual relationship, the two became lovers.

"The only way to get rid of temptation is to yield to it... I can resist everything but temptation."

In 1895, Bosie's father accused Wilde of homosexuality and, rather foolishly, Wilde tried to sue him for libel. Although Wilde soon withdrew his libel case, he was subsequently arrested and convicted for gross indecency, receiving a sentence of two years' hard labour to be served at Wandsworth Prison.

Declared bankrupt while in prison, Wilde was generally abandoned by his friends and loved ones. His wife, Constance, took the children to Switzerland and changed her name to Holland. He never saw his two sons again.

His time at Wandsworth Prison was tough. His requests for books and writing material were denied. He slept on a hard wooden bed and had to endure six hours a day exercising on the prison treadmill. Matters eased for him when he was transferred to Reading Gaol, where he was allowed to resume his writing. He set down his thoughts in an autobiographical essay, *De Profundis* (see page opposite), which he addressed to Bosie as a letter of accusation. He was in an obvious state of despair while in prison, and reading *De Profundis* gives an

Oscar Wilde and Lord Alfred "Bosie" Douglas

© National Portrait Gallery, London

insight into his tormented soul — particularly over his great sadness at the loss of his mother, just three months into his prison sentence. He describes how Constance travelled from Genoa in a state of ill health in order to break the sad news of his mother's death to him in person. Constance herself died in 1898.

"One of the many lessons that one learns in prison is, that things are what they are and will be what they will be."

When he was released in 1897, Wilde wrote *The Ballad of Reading Gaol* in which he expressed his concerns for the poor prison conditions; but his personal reputation had been destroyed by the whole affair, and he was no longer popular. He wandered

around Europe, divorced and bankrupt. He took the name Sebastian Melmoth and stayed with friends or in cheap hotels. His new surname was from the gothic horror novel *Melmoth the Wanderer* by Wilde's great-uncle, Charles Robert Maturin, in which Melmoth sells his soul to the devil in exchange for another 150 years of life.

Under these rough living conditions, Wilde's health soon deteriorated. He suffered from a recurrent ear infection and eventually died of cerebral meningitis in Paris on 30th November 1900. For one who brought so much enjoyment into the world through his work and his wit, it is desperately sad that, from the heights of celebrity, he should die a broken, penniless man.

De Profundis

Wilde was initially denied books and writing materials during his prison sentence, but these were finally granted when he was transferred from Wandsworth Prison to Reading Gaol. There, he was allowed to write up to one page a day, to be handed over to the prison warden each night. It was under those conditions that he set his thoughts down on paper in an autobiographical essay. This heartfelt and sincere work was eventually published after his death under the title *De Profundis*. Here is an extract from it:

Suffering is one very long moment. We cannot divide it by seasons. We can only record its moods, and chronicle their return. With us time itself does not progress. It revolves. It seems to circle round one centre of pain. The paralysing immobility of a life every circumstance of which is regulated after an unchangeable pattern, so that we eat and drink and lie down and pray, or kneel at least for prayer, according to the inflexible laws of an iron formula: this immobile quality, that makes each dreadful day in the very minutest detail like its brother, seems to communicate itself to those external forces the very essence of whose existence is ceaseless change. Of seed–time or harvest, of the reapers bending over the corn, or the grape gatherers threading through the vines, of the grass in the orchard made white with broken blossoms or strewn with fallen fruit: of these we know nothing and can know nothing.

For us there is only one season, the season of sorrow. The very sun and moon seem taken from us. Outside, the day may be blue and gold, but the light that creeps down through the thickly–muffled glass of the small iron–barred window beneath which one sits is grey and niggard. It is always twilight in one's cell, as it is always twilight in one's heart. And in the sphere of thought, no less than in the sphere of time, motion is no more. The thing that you personally have long ago forgotten, or can easily forget, is happening to me now, and will happen to me again to–morrow.

Remember this, and you will be able to understand a little of why I am writing, and in this manner writing...

A week later, I am transferred here. Three more months go over and my mother dies. No one knew how deeply I loved and honoured her. Her death was terrible to me; but I, once a lord of language, have no words in which to express my anguish and my shame. She and my father had bequeathed me a name they had made noble and honoured, not merely in literature, art, archaeology, and science, but in the public history of my own country, in its evolution as a nation. I had disgraced that name eternally. I had made it a low by–word among low people. I had dragged it through the very mire. I had given it to brutes that they might make it brutal, and to fools that they might turn it into a synonym for folly.

What I suffered then, and still suffer, is not for pen to write or paper to record. My wife, always kind and gentle to me, rather than that I should hear the news from indifferent lips, travelled, ill as she was, all the way from Genoa to England to break to me herself the tidings of so irreparable, so irremediable, a loss. Messages of sympathy reached me from all who had still affection for me. Even people who had not known me personally, hearing that a new sorrow had broken into my life, wrote to ask that some expression of their condolence should be conveyed to me...

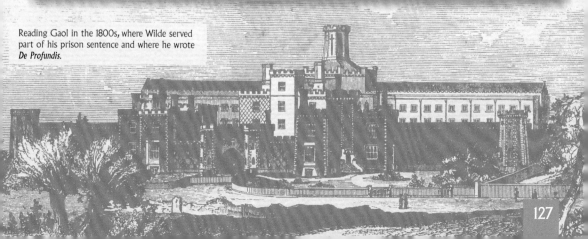

Reading Gaol in the 1800s, where Wilde served part of his prison sentence and where he wrote *De Profundis*.

Wilde Timeline

1854
Oscar Fingal O'Flahertie Wills Wilde born in Dublin, Ireland, on 16th February.

1864
Attends boarding school at Portora Royal School, Enniskillen.

1871
Returns to Dublin to read Classics at Trinity College.

1872
Awarded foundation scholarship.

1874
Awarded Berkeley Gold Medal for Greek and is awarded Demyship scholarship to attend Magdalen College, Oxford.

1876
His father, Sir William Wilde, dies at the age of 61. His mother, Lady Jane Francesca Wilde (aged 56), moves to Chelsea, London, for a more active social life.

1878
Wins Newdigate Prize for his poem *Ravenna*. Graduates from Magdalen College with first class honours.

1879
Settles in London and spends time socialising with, amongst others, the society belle and actress, Lily Langtree.

1881
Self-publishes *Poems*, a collection of his poetry. His fame grows as a personality, wit and popular member of London society.

1882
Lecture tour of America and Canada to promote *Poems* and the Aesthetic movement.

1883
Attends the first night of his play, *Vera*, in New York. The play is not a success and quickly folds.

1884
Marries Constance Lloyd (also originally from Dublin).

1885
First son, Cyril, born.

1886
Second son, Vyvyan, born.

1887
Financial pressures force Wilde to take the job of editor at *Woman's World* magazine.
Writes *The Canterville Ghost* — a short story, and his most important work to this date. It proves to be a turning point in his literary career.

1888
Publishes *The Happy Prince and Other Tales*, a collection of fairy stories written for his two sons.

1890
The Picture of Dorian Gray is serialised in *Lippincott's Magazine*. It shocks many readers and goes on to become his only novel.

1891
Publishes *Lord Arthur Savile's Crime and Other Stories* (which included *The Canterville Ghost*) Also publishes a second version of *The Picture of Dorian Gray*.
Meets the poet Lord Alfred "Bosie" Douglas (the third son of the Marquess of Queensbury) and they start a close relationship.

1892
His play *Lady Windermere's Fan* opens to great critical acclaim. Its success brings wealth and wide popularity.

1893
Writes the first of a series of comic plays, *A Woman of No Importance*.
His marriage to Constance effectively comes to an end.

1894
Completes his next play, *An Ideal Husband*.

1895
Completes his most popular comic play, *The Importance of Being Earnest*.
Accused of homosexuality by the father of Lord Alfred "Bosie" Douglas. Arrested and convicted of gross indecency. Sentenced to two years' hard labour. Declared bankrupt. His wife and children move to Switzerland.

1896
His mother dies while he is in Reading Gaol. His wife, Constance, travels back from Switzerland to break the news to him personally.

1897
Released from prison, he travels around Europe. Financially ruined and a broken man, he adopts a new name — Sebastian Melmoth, after the hero of the gothic novel *Melmoth the Wanderer* (written by his great-uncle) and Saint Sebastian, the saint who was martyred twice.

1898
His wife Constance dies.
His poem *The Ballad of Reading Gaol* is published.

1900
Dies of cerebral meningitis in Paris on 30th November.

"If another century began and I was still alive, it would really be more than the English could stand."

The Canterville Ghost is Born

Oscar Wilde's short story, *The Canterville Ghost – A Hylo–Idealistic Romance*, first appeared in serialised form in 1887, in the magazine *Court and Society Review*. It was later published in 1891 within a collection of short stories entitled *Lord Arthur Savile's Crime and Other Stories*.

Culture Clash

Five years prior to writing the story, Wilde had toured America and Canada to deliver a series of lectures (see page 131). That tour gave him the opportunity to witness the differences between British and American ways of life. In *The Canterville Ghost*, Wilde pitched representatives from each culture against each other, setting the New World against the Old. The British ghost is always talking of past exploits and revelling in former glories. The members of the American Otis family, on the other hand, have little regard for the past and are coldly practical and materialistic. It is up to the daughter of the family, the pure of heart and innocent Virginia Otis, to mediate between the two worlds and bring about peace.

The First Gothic Horror Comedy

The gothic horror genre was immensely popular in the late 1800s. Advances in printing had made books affordable for the first time, and today's world of mass media was born. The century had already seen the publication of many gothic horror masterpieces such as *Frankenstein* and *Dracula*, which mostly followed the familiar format of the supernatural terrorising the mortal. For comedic effect, however, Wilde turned this situation on its head – it is the ghost who is persecuted and made to suffer at the hands of the mortals. In so doing, Wilde had effectively written the first gothic horror comedy.

Theatrical Life

While he was yet to enjoy success as a playwright, Wilde was already fully immersed in the world of the theatre. As a leading figure of the Aesthetic Movement (see page 130) he promoted "art for art sake", believing that an artist's greatest work should be their life, not any of the pieces of art that they create. This is the basis for the ghost's character, Sir Simon de Canterville, who plays the part of many roles. Throughout the entire story he uses theatrical terms such as costumes, performances, debuts, roles and appearances. The ghost's very existence is in keeping with the philosophies of the Aesthetic Movement, being one, big, artistic performance.

However, every performance needs an audience, and, frustratingly for the ghost, the Otis family are unreceptive to his carryings on. Instead of being scared, they simply view the ghost as a nuisance and (in the case of the twins) something to torment. For the first time in his supernatural life as a performance artist, the ghost is struggling to have any effect on his audience. He doesn't know what to do and, because of the way the story is written, we end up feeling sorry for the ghost as we would for any actor being rejected by an audience.

Adaptations

Although Wilde never wrote a version of *The Canterville Ghost* for the theatre, the story lends itself well to dramatic adaptation.

The story appeared as a movie for the first time in 1944, with the plot amended so that part of it was set in World War II.

Adaptations that are more authentic to Wilde's original story have appeared since, most notably the films of 1986, starring Sir John Gielgud, and 1995, featuring Sir Patrick Stewart.

Now, for the first time in its history, this wonderful story appears as a full-colour graphic novel!

The Aesthetic Movement

The Aesthetic Movement was an idea in art, design and literature towards the end of the nineteenth century that considered aesthetic values to be more important than anything else. Its origins lay in the writings of the philosopher Immanuel Kant (1724-1804), who believed that art should exist for its own sake and should not be created purely to bring pleasure to others. This was captured by the phrase "art for art's sake" which became associated with the movement.

Although Oscar Wilde was not a founder of the movement, he promoted it heavily and embodied its beliefs. As with most things, Wilde took the ideas of the movement further than most. He believed that the lives of artists should be their greatest artistic work and, as art, should not be constrained or governed by morality, conformity, or convention. Artists should be free to express themselves in all aspects of their life, with that expression being itself a work of art.

Needless to say, the Aesthetic Movement was often ridiculed. The popular light-opera writers of the day, Gilbert and Sullivan, enjoyed huge success with their satirical play, *Patience,* which mocked the Aesthetes. The play's central character was called Reginald Bunthorne – a dandy with long hair, knee breeches and silk stockings, with an obsession for lilies and sunflowers. To the public, this character was Oscar Wilde himself – to the point that Wilde gained the reputation for doing things in real life that Bunthorne had merely done in fiction, such as walking down Piccadilly with a lily in his hand.

The principles of the Aesthetic Movement are present in *The Canterville Ghost.* Wilde has the central character putting on all sorts of theatrical performances; indeed, the ghost's whole existence is one long piece of performance art, in keeping with the beliefs of the Aesthetic Movement. The ghost cannot understand why his art is not being appreciated by his audience (the Otis family), who see his actions merely as a nuisance.

It is generally accepted that the Aesthetic Movement came to an end in 1895, when Wilde was convicted and imprisoned for gross indecency. With that event, the movement lost its figurehead. Wilde's time in prison affected him greatly; yet he continued to live by the values of the Aesthetic Movement when he was released, considering his whole life to be one grand artistic gesture. As he said of himself,

"I have put my genius into my life and only my talent into my work".

Wilde in America

Having graduated with first class honours from Magdalen College, Oxford, a twenty-seven-year-old Oscar Wilde arrived in New York on 2nd January 1882, to embark on a lecture tour of America and Canada. He was originally scheduled to deliver fifty lectures in four months promoting the Aesthetic Movement (see page opposite), but he was such a success that he ended up delivering 140 lectures in nearly nine months.

Wilde was the figurehead of the Aesthetic Movement. With his dandy persona and sharp wit, he was the perfect advertisement for the benefit of aesthetics, and he was quite a celebrity. His entourage included three secretaries:

"One writes my autographs all day for my admirers, the other receives the flowers that are left really every ten minutes. A third whose hair resembles mine is obliged to send off locks of his own hair to the myriad maidens of the city, and so is rapidly becoming bald."

The timing of Wilde's lecture tour coincided with a deep interest in the Aesthetic Movement, spurred on by the Gilbert and Sullivan play *Patience* that satirised people like Wilde as dandy wearers of knee breeches and stockings. When sixty students dressed in that manner to attend his lecture in Boston, Wilde appeared in a respectable dress suit saying, to huge applause,

"Caricature is the tribute that mediocrity pays to genius".

(excerpts from) *Impressions of America* (1882)

The first thing that struck me on landing in America was that if the Americans are not the most well-dressed people in the world, they are the most comfortably dressed.

The next thing particularly noticeable is that everybody seems in a hurry to catch a train. This is a state of things which is not favourable to poetry or romance. Had Romeo or Juliet been in a constant state of anxiety about trains, or had their minds been agitated by the question of return–tickets, Shakespeare could not have given us those lovely balcony scenes which are so full of poetry and pathos.

America is the noisiest country that ever existed. One is waked up in the morning, not by the singing of the nightingale, but by the steam whistle.

A remarkable characteristic of the Americans is the manner in which they have applied science to modern life. In England an inventor is regarded almost as a crazy man, and in too many instances invention ends in disappointment and poverty. In America an inventor is honoured, help is forthcoming, and the exercise of ingenuity, the application of science to the work of man, is there the shortest road to wealth.

From Salt Lake City one travels over great plains of Colorado and up the Rocky Mountains, on the top of which is Leadville, the richest city in the world. It has also got the reputation of being the roughest, and every man carries a revolver. I was told that if I went there they would be sure to shoot me or my travelling manager. They are miners—men working in metals, so I lectured them on the Ethics of Art. I read them passages from the autobiography of Benvenuto Cellini and they seemed much delighted. I was reproved by my hearers for not having brought him with me. I explained that he had been dead for some little time which elicited the enquiry "Who shot him?". They afterwards took me to a dancing saloon where I saw the only rational method of art criticism I have ever come across. Over the piano was printed a notice:

Please do not shoot the pianist.
He is doing his best.

In going to America one learns that poverty is not a necessary accompaniment to civilisation. There at any rate is a country that has no trappings, no pageants and no gorgeous ceremonies. I saw only two processions—one was the Fire Brigade preceded by the Police, the other was the Police preceded by the Fire Brigade.

Page Creation

Here we take a page from the book and show what went on "behind the scenes" to create it and bring *The Canterville Ghost* to life.

The Script

Much like a stage play, the first task in creating a graphic novel adaptation is to write a script from the original story. It is a fascinating stage that sets the tone for the whole book. The scriptwriter (Seán Michael Wilson in this case) takes the prose text and decides how each panel will look. To do this well he needs to visualise each page before the artist has drawn anything, to create a "blueprint in words".

PAGE 112		
PANEL 1: Otis appeals to Lord Canterville.		
	ORIGINAL TEXT	QUICK TEXT
Otis	Under these circumstances, Lord Canterville, I feel sure that you will recognise how impossible it would be for me to allow them to remain in the possession of any member of my family;	Therefore, Lord Canterville, the gems cannot remain in the possession of my family.
PANEL 2: Otis looks out of the window, hands behind his back, getting pompous on his soapbox. Behind him, Lord Canterville is sniggering and laughing at what he is saying (in a nice way).		
Otis	and, indeed, all such vain gauds and toys, however suitable or necessary to the dignity of the British aristocracy, would be completely out of place among those who have been brought up on the severe, and I believe immortal, principles of Republican simplicity.	All such decorations, necessary to the British gentry, would be out of place with we who have been raised on the principles of Republican simplicity.
PANEL 3: Otis returns to the table, and closes the lid on the box.		
Otis	Perhaps I should mention that Virginia is very anxious that you should allow her to retain the box, as a memento of your unfortunate but misguided ancestor. As it is extremely old, and consequently a good deal out of repair, you may perhaps think fit to comply with her request.	However, Virginia would very much like to keep the box as a memento. It is quite shabby, so I hope you can agree to that.

Our graphic novel of *The Canterville Ghost* is available in two text versions: Original Text and Quick Text (see page opposite for example). While the text between them differs, the images remain the same. Therefore, in this extract from the script, we have a single set of panel descriptions along with two sets of captions and dialogue, one for each text edition of the graphic novel.

The Rough Sketch

Sometimes called a "thumbnail sketch" because it is usually drawn small, the rough sketch is probably the most critical stage of each page. As you can see in this example, the page is worked on very loosely and quickly, to make sure the storytelling is in place. Storytelling is the "art within the art" that is key to the graphic narrative: drawing

people is one thing, but the way that they stand, their posture and expression makes for real storytelling. It is amazing how few lines are required to depict the essence of the page, but it is always worthwhile having notes such as Lord Canterville sniggering in the background. On a practical note, it is also vital that enough room will be left for the lettering.

The Pencil Stage

Because this particular page was created digitally, there is no actual pencil stage where the images are drawn in pencil onto artboard. However, the rough layouts

still need to be drawn more accurately, making sure that anatomy and proportions are correct. There is no real detail at this point because having clean lines helps to highlight any inaccuracies in the drawing.

As you can see, the pencils have stayed close to the rough sketch, except that Lord Canterville has moved further away from Mr. Otis so that his sniggering cannot be overheard.

The Inking Stage

Again working digitally in the case of this page, a variety of digital brushes are used to clarify the "pencil" lines. This is where texture and shadows are added to each surface and a variance of line thicknesses employed to give the impression of depth in the image.

You can see the folds and ripples in Mr. Otis's clothing in the first panel, while the walls and window frames are textured to look like stone. The window panes themselves are indicated by three "dash" lines each, and the view outside is a vague rendition of distant trees and meadow. The scenes begin to take on depth and substance in the inking stage.

The Colouring Stage

Colouring is where the image really comes to life. The skill in colouring is not to simply fill the white space with the right colour, but also to create form, giving the impression of three dimensions on the two dimensional plane. The inked folds in Mr. Otis's jacket have been accentuated, his skin tones cleverly rendered, and hair shadows added to make

the figure look more life-like. Additionally, features such as the shading on the wall in panel two, capturing the falling light from the window, add to the realism. There is also a lovely touch in the last panel where a single gem in the jewellery box has been picked out with a sharp burst of light.

Lettering

The final stage is to add the captions, speech balloons and sound effects from the script, remembering that there are two versions of each page: Original Text and Quick Text. When deciding on the placement of the balloons, the letterer not only has to adhere to comic book lettering conventions, but also must consider the way the reader's eyes will move over the page. There is a flow to great lettering that makes it natural and comfortable to read, to the point that the text becomes part of the art.

Once all that is done for each page, the artwork and lettering can then be compiled into the finished book.

Original Text

ISBN:
978-1-906332-27-3

THE CLASSIC STORY
BROUGHT TO LIFE IN FULL COLOUR!

Quick Text

ISBN:
978-1-906332-28-0

THE FULL STORY IN QUICK MODERN
ENGLISH FOR A FAST-PACED READ!

MORE TITLES AVAILABLE FROM

Shakespeare's plays in a choice of 3 text versions. Simply choose the text version to match your reading level.

Original Text — THE ENTIRE SHAKESPEARE PLAY - UNABRIDGED!

Plain Text — THE ENTIRE PLAY TRANSLATED INTO PLAIN ENGLISH!

Quick Text — THE ENTIRE PLAY IN QUICK MODERN ENGLISH FOR A FAST-PACED READ!

Macbeth: The Graphic Novel (William Shakespeare)
- Script Adaptation: John McDonald • Pencils: & Inks: Jon Haward
- Inking Assistant: Gary Erskine • Colours & Letters: Nigel Dobbyn   **144 Pages • £9.99**

ISBN: 978-1-906332-03-7   ISBN: 978-1-906332-04-4   ISBN: 978-1-906332-05-1

Romeo & Juliet: The Graphic Novel (William Shakespeare)
- Script Adaptation: John McDonald • Linework: Will Volley
- Colours: Jim Devlin • Letters: Jim Campbell   **168 Pages • £9.99**

ISBN: 978-1-906332-19-8   ISBN: 978-1-906332-20-4   ISBN: 978-1-906332-21-1

The Tempest: The Graphic Novel (William Shakespeare)
- Script Adaptation: John McDonald • Pencils: Jon Haward
- Inks: Gary Erskine • Colours: & Letters: Nigel Dobbyn   **144 Pages • £9.99**

ISBN: 978-1-906332-29-7   ISBN: 978-1-906332-30-3   ISBN: 978-1-906332-31-0

Henry V: The Graphic Novel (William Shakespeare)
- Script Adaptation: John McDonald • Pencils: Neill Cameron • Inks: Bambos
- Colours: Jason Cardy & Kat Nicholson • Letters: Nigel Dobbyn   **144 Pages • £9.99**

ISBN: 978-1-906332-00-6   ISBN: 978-1-906332-01-3   ISBN: 978-1-906332-02-0

UR AWARD-WINNING RANGE

Classic Literature in a choice of 2 text versions. Simply choose the text version to match your reading level.

Original Text THE CLASSIC NOVEL BROUGHT TO LIFE IN FULL COLOUR!

Quick Text THE FULL STORY IN QUICK MODERN ENGLISH FOR A FAST-PACED READ!

Frankenstein: The Graphic Novel (Mary Shelley)

- Script Adaptation: Jason Cobley • Linework: Declan Shalvey • Art Direction: Jon Haward
- Colours: Jason Cardy & Kat Nicholson • Letters: Terry Wiley

"Cursed be the hands that formed you!"

ISBN: 978-1-906332-15-0 ISBN: 978-1-906332-16-7

• 144 Pages • £9.99

Jane Eyre: The Graphic Novel (Charlotte Brontë)

- Script Adaptation: Amy Corzine • Artwork: John M. Burns
- Letters: Terry Wiley

"I scorn your idea of love and the counterfeit sentiment you offer. And I scorn you when you offer it."

ISBN: 978-1-906332-06-8 ISBN: 978-1-906332-08-2

• 144 Pages • £9.99

A Christmas Carol: The Graphic Novel (Charles Dickens)

- Script Adaptation: Seán Michael Wilson • Pencils: Mike Collins
- Inks: David Roach • Colours: James Offredi • Letters: Terry Wiley

"I will honour Christmas in my heart, and try to keep it all the year. I will live in the Past, the Present, and the Future."

ISBN: 978-1-906332-17-4 ISBN: 978-1-906332-18-1

• 160 Pages • £9.99

Great Expectations: The Graphic Novel (Charles Dickens)

- Script Adaptation: Jen Green • Linework: John Stokes • Colouring: Digikore Studios Ltd
- Colour Finishing: Jason Cardy • Letters: Jim Campbell

"I never saw my father or my mother, and never saw any likeness of either of them."

ISBN: 978-1-906332-09-9 ISBN: 978-1-906332-11-2

• 160 Pages • £9.99

To see the complete range, and to view samples online, go to www.classicalcomics.com

The Canterville Ghost Teaching Resource Pack

ISBN: 978-1-906332-84-6

Helping you prepare motivating and stimulating lessons

- Over 100 spiral-bound, photocopiable pages.
- Cross-curricular topics and activities.
- Ideal for differentiated teaching.

- CD includes an electronic version of the teaching book for whiteboards, laptops and digital printing.
- Only £19.99

To accompany each title in our series of graphic novels and to help with their application in the classroom, we also publish teaching resource packs. These widely acclaimed 100+ page books are spiral-bound, making the pages easy to photocopy. They also include a CD-ROM with the pages in

PDF format, ideal for whole-class teaching on whiteboards, laptops, etc or for direct digital printing. These books are written by teachers, for teachers, helping students to engage in the play or novel. Suitable for teaching ages 10-17, each book provides exercises that cover structure,

listening, understanding, motivation and character as well as key words, themes and literary techniques. Devised to encompass a broad range of skill levels, they provide many opportunities for differentiated teaching and the tailoring of lessons to meet individual needs.

DVD-ROM with full audio!

Macbeth

THE INTERACTIVE MOTION COMIC

Macbeth – The Interactive Motion Comic makes teaching and learning Shakespeare's most famous play EASY! Unlike any motion comic before, this animated graphic novel from Classical Comics boasts a full-audio soundtrack, helpful context notes, and allows easy switching between text versions to help students of all levels to understand and enjoy the play.

THE ENTIRE SHAKESPEARE PLAY - UNABRIDGED!

THE ENTIRE PLAY - TRANSLATED INTO PLAIN ENGLISH!

THE ENTIRE PLAY - IN QUICK MODERN ENGLISH FOR A FAST-PACED READ!

✓ Professional voice actors, including the talents of **Sir Derek Jacobi** and **Juliet Stevenson** in the title roles.

✓ Links to the *Macbeth* Classical Comics graphic novels.

✓ Includes Act / Scene / Line references to link with any traditional script.

✓ Go through panel-by-panel, or choose "Movie Mode" to watch the whole play unfold!

For an online preview visit www.classicalcomics.com / imacbeth